SEMI-CONDUCTORS

Semi-conductors have become of great technical importance during recent years, and are finding an increasing number of applications. This book gives an elementary account of their basic physical properties, and of the principles of rectifiers, transistors, thermistors and devices based on photoconductivity, on the Hall effect, and on thermoelectricity. The most important materials used for thermionic emission, secondary emission and photo-electric emission are semi-conductors, and their properties are also included.

The book has been brought thoroughly up to date for this edition.

SCIENCE PAPERBACKS

SP 5

SEMI-CONDUCTORS

Professor D. A. Wright
D. Sc., M. Sc., F. Inst. P.

Department of Applied Physics
The University of Durham

SCIENCE PAPERBACKS

& METHUEN & CO LTD

First published 1950 *by Methuen & Co Ltd*
First published in this series (*Fourth edition*) 1966

©1966 *by D. A. Wright*

Printed in Great Britain by
Spottiswoode Ballantyne & Co Ltd
London and Colchester

SCIENCE PAPERBACKS

are published by Chapman & Hall Ltd
Methuen & Co Ltd E. & F. N. Spon
all members of Associated Book Publishers Ltd
11 New Fetter Lane, London EC4

Preface

The object of this book is to give an elementary account of the properties of semi-conductors. Since the book was first published (1950) there have been important advances in the physics of solids in general and of semi-conductors in particular, and there have been at the same time large-scale developments in the application of semi-conductors. The book has been considerably revised in the present edition, though the author is well aware that there remain many omissions. No attempt is made to deal with the preparation either of materials or of devices, nor is there any indication of the historical development of the subject.

This monograph can be regarded only as a brief introduction, and further reading will be essential for serious students. There are now many textbooks on semi-conductors, numerous survey articles and conference reports, and a very large number of papers in the scientific journals. Reference is made to many of the textbooks, but to only a few of the papers. The papers selected are those which seem particularly relevant to the text; they are not necessarily the most important from a historical point of view.

ERRATA

page 9, line 26:

$$E = \tfrac{3}{5} W \left(1 + \frac{5}{12} \frac{\pi^2 k^2 T^2}{W^2} \right)$$

to read

$$E = \tfrac{3}{5} W \left(1 + \frac{5}{12} \frac{\pi^2 k^2 T^2}{W^2} \right)$$

Page 63, line 4:

$$V^H \text{ to read } V_H.$$

Page 95, line 13:

$$= \sqrt{D_p/\tau_p}, \text{ to read } = \sqrt{D_p/\tau_p},$$

Contents

CHAPTER 1

Electrons in Solids

The free-electron model

1. *Introduction.* Before proceeding to a discussion of non-metallic solids, it will be necessary to survey briefly the elementary treatment of metals, with special reference to those properties which determine electron flow in the solid and across boundaries between different solids or between a solid and a vacuum. The results of this treatment of the metallic case will be required in deriving the corresponding properties of semi-conductors, and comparison of the results in the two cases will be of interest. It is necessary first to introduce the conception of the energy levels of electrons in a solid, which is invoked continuously in the remainder of the book.

2. *Potential Energy of Electrons in a Solid.* When considering the motion of electrons, both in a solid and when escaping from its surface, it is convenient to draw potential-energy diagrams, since the motion of the electrons can be regarded to a first approximation as that of particles in a conservative field of force. A simple case to consider by way of introduction is that of a pendulum bob, in which the potential energy V varies with displacement as in Fig. 1. A particle with total energy H_1 will have potential energy H_1 and kinetic energy zero when the displacement is OB. The kinetic energy will have its maximum value H_1 at zero displacement, and intermediately the potential energy at displacement OA is given by AP. The motion is restricted to that region in which the potential energy V is less than or equal to the total energy H.

It is known experimentally that in order to liberate electrons from a solid, energy must be provided, for example, by heating, by incident radiation, or by bombardment with electrons or other particles. A solid can therefore be represented by a potential-energy diagram as in Fig. 2, in which O is the potential-energy level outside the solid, and A is the corresponding lower level for an electron in the solid. Thus, when the electron is regarded as a particle in classical mechanics, it will remain in motion inside the solid when its kinetic energy is in the range from zero to AO, for example, if it is AB. If, however, an electron has kinetic energy AC, it can escape from the solid, and outside the solid it will have kinetic energy OC. At room temperature

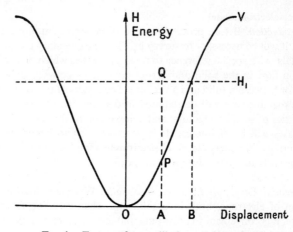

FIG. 1.—Energy of an oscillating pendulum bob

in the dark, very few electrons have total energy greater than AO in any solid, but the number increases with temperature, leading to thermionic emission, while incident light or particles can interact with an electron of kinetic energy AB, increasing it to AC, and so permitting the escape of the electron. This corresponds with photo-electric emission in the case of incident radiation and secondary emission in the case of incident particles.

In considering the behaviour of electrons in a solid in greater detail, it is necessary to have information concerning the number of electrons in motion and the way in which their energies are distributed. In the case of a metal, the simplest assumption is that the metal atoms, arranged in the crystal lattice lose their valence electrons, in the sense that these electrons do not remain attached to particular atoms, but are free to wander in the crystal. If the field of the positive ions is smoothed out, and its local, very violent fluctuations are disregarded, the electrons can be regarded as completely free, and can be considered as an 'electron gas'. Since the total field on one electron is that due to the N positive ions in the crystal and the $N{-}1$ other electrons, this smoothing out gives a good first approximation. Since there are one or more valence electrons per atom, there will be of the order 10^{22} free electrons per cm^3 in the crystal. Their energy distribution will be determined by application of quantum theory and the exclusion principle. The states of motion in which electrons can exist correspond

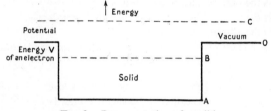

FIG. 2.—Representation of a solid

with discrete energy levels as in a single atom, but the levels are very close together. Nevertheless, the exclusion principle applies, and no more than two electrons (of opposite spins) can be in exactly the same energy state. In applying the quantum rules, we are departing from the concept of an electron as a particle in classical mechanics, and are using the consequences of the wave picture which will be referred to again below. The consequence of the exclusion principle is that even at the absolute zero of temperature, energy levels are occupied by two electrons each, from the zero of kinetic energy to some value W, which is typical of the particular metal. When the temperature is raised, it is only possible for electrons in the highest occupied levels to gain energy until they occupy higher levels, which were unoccupied at zero temperature. Thus only a small proportion of the total free electrons, the fast-moving ones, gain energy when the temperature is raised.

3. *Fermi–Dirac Statistics*. The energy distribution described above is described mathematically by the Fermi–Dirac statistics, which are based on the exclusion principle and on the indistinguishability of electrons.[1] The result is

$$\delta n_E = \frac{4\pi(2m)^{3/2}}{h^3} \frac{E^{1/2}\,\delta E}{e^{(E-W)/kT}+1} \qquad (1.1)$$

where

δn_E is the number of electrons per cm^3 with energy between E and $E+\delta E$,

m is the mass of the electron $= 9\cdot107 \cdot 10^{-28}$ g.

h is Planck's constant $= 6\cdot624 \cdot 10^{-27}$ erg-sec.

e is the base of natural logarithms $= 2\cdot718$.

k is Boltzmann's constant $= 1\cdot381 \cdot 10^{-16}$ erg/degree.

T is the absolute temperature in $^\circ K$.

W is an energy which, as will appear below, can be identified with the energy W in Figs. 3 and 5.

$[4\pi(2m)^{3/2}/h^3]E^{1/2}\delta E$ is the density of energy levels per cm^3 in the range E to $E+\delta E$, also called the density of states. $1/(1+e^{(E-W)/kT})$ is the probability that a level or state with energy E is occupied by an electron.

This distribution can also be expressed in terms of momentum p, giving δn_p, the number of electrons with momentum between p and $p+\delta p$, as

$$\delta n_p = \frac{8\pi}{h^3}\frac{p^2\,\delta p}{e^{(E-W)/kT}+1} \qquad (1.2)$$

It is clear that when T is zero, the value of δn_E in (1.1) becomes zero when $E > W$, and has the value $[4\pi(2m)^{3/2}E^{1/2}\delta E]/h^3$ when $E < W$. W is therefore the limiting value of the energy, which is not exceeded at zero temperature. It is called the Fermi level. The distribution function therefore follows a half-power law, until $E = W$, when it falls to zero, as in Fig. 3. At a higher temperature, the function follows the dotted curve, showing that a few electrons have energy greater than W.

If the number of electrons is N/cm^3, the fitting in of this density of electrons into the available number of energy states gives for the height of the Fermi level when T is zero:

$$W = \frac{h^2}{2m}\left(\frac{3N}{8\pi}\right)^{2/3} \tag{1.3}$$

At other temperatures, the Fermi level is at a slightly different height W_T given by

$$W_T = W\left(1 - \frac{\pi^2 k^2 T^2}{12 W^2} + \ldots\right) \tag{1.4}$$

It is then the energy at which the probability of occupation is a half.

It is convenient here to introduce the electron volt as a unit of energy. It is the energy acquired by an electron in falling through a potential difference of 1 volt, and has the value $1 \cdot 602\ 10^{-12}$ erg. We find that when $N = 10^{21}$, W is $0 \cdot 38$ eV, and when $N = 10^{23}$, W is $8 \cdot 2$ eV. Thus for different metals, W is of the order of a few electron volts, and varies with the atomic spacing and valency.

It is important to notice that in some situations the unity in the denominator in 1.1 or 1.2 can be neglected compared with $e^{(E-W)/kT}$. If W/kT is zero or positive, the unity can be neglected only over a range of values of E such that $(E - W)/kT > 2$. If W is sufficiently negative however, it becomes possible to neglect the unity at all values of E (since E is kinetic energy, all its values are positive). This leads to accurate expressions if $W/kT < -2$. For positive values of W the omission of the unity simplifies integration, while for negative values of W the consequence is to give the Maxwell–Boltzmann statistics rather than the Fermi statistics. Thus 1.1 becomes

$$\delta n_E = \frac{4 \cdot (2\pi m)^{3/2}}{\pi^{1/2}} \frac{e^{W/kT} E^{1/2}}{h^3} e^{-E/kT} \delta E$$

When this is integrated and made equal to N, it is found that $e^{W/kT}$ has the value

$$\frac{Nh^3}{2(2\pi m kT)^{3/2}} \tag{1.5}$$

and in this case

$$\delta n_E = \frac{2\pi N}{(\pi kT)^{3/2}} E^{1/2} e^{-E/kT} \delta E \tag{1.6}$$

This is the same as the Maxwellian distribution for a 'gas' of particles of mass m at temperature T, and is evidently encountered when the expression (1.5) is less than unity, corresponding with negative values of W/kT. This will occur when N is small or when T is large. When N is as large as $10^{22}/cm^3$, 1.5 is of the order 100 even when T approaches $4000°K$, so that the electron gas in a metal obeys the Fermi–Dirac statistics at all temperatures at which metals remain solid. Such an electron gas is called 'degenerate'. In fact when expression 1.5 has a value greater than unity, it does not give the correct value of W, which must be determined from 1.3. The value of 1.5 becomes less than unity for electrons at ordinary temperatures

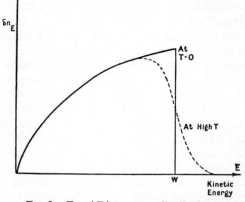

FIG. 3.—Fermi-Dirac energy distribution.

when N is less than $10^{19}/cm^3$ and the 'gas' is then non-degenerate, it obeys Maxwell–Boltzmann statistics, and W/kT is accurately determined by (1.5).

4. *Electrical Conductivity.* It is supposed that the electrons at temperature T in the absence of an electric field move randomly in the solid, suffering collisions such that there is a mean free path l_0. When an electric field is applied, there is a drift velocity u superposed on the random velocity. The free path is terminated by a collision, i.e. a

scattering process, and the drift velocity acquired during the path length is assumed lost at the collision.

An electric field X produces on any electron a force $-\epsilon X$ and an acceleration $-\epsilon X/m$. For any individual drift velocity, or for the average drift velocity u, we can write:

$$\partial u/\partial t = -\frac{\epsilon X}{m}$$

The current density J will be $-\epsilon N u$, where N is the number of electrons per cm³. The values of J and N for metals indicate that u is normally small compared with the thermal velocities. To be consistent with Ohm's law, we know that u must normally be proportional to X, i.e. that the electrons are not accelerated indefinitely. Thus there must be an opposing force which leads to zero net acceleration in the steady state with the field applied. This must arise from the scattering processes and must be the force which restores the electron energy distribution to its state dependent only on temperature when the electric field is removed.

This situation is described in terms of a relaxation time $\tau^{(2)}$, which determines how the drift velocity u decays to zero; t seconds after switching off the field, the drift velocity is $u_t = u\mathrm{e}^{-t/\tau}$. This indicates that:

$$\partial u/\partial t = -u/\tau$$

Thus the net acceleration with the field applied is $-\epsilon X/m - u/\tau$, and since a steady drift velocity is set up, this must be zero. This leads to the relation

$$u = -\frac{\epsilon \tau X}{m} \qquad (1.7)$$

From this there follows the definition of the mobility u_0, the drift velocity in unit field:

$$u_0 = -\frac{\epsilon \tau}{m} \qquad (1.8)$$

The current density is therefore given by:

$$J = \frac{N\epsilon^2 \tau X}{m} \qquad (1.9)$$

2

and the electrical conductivity by:

$$\sigma = \frac{N\epsilon^2\tau}{m} \qquad (1.10)$$

In the simplest case when the scattering process is independent of the direction of motion of the electron relative to the field, τ is the same as the mean time between collisions, given by l_0/v, where v is the average velocity of the thermal motion.

In metals we have seen above that the electrons which can be affected by changes in temperature are those at the top of the Fermi distribution. The same is true when we consider the effect of applying an electric field. Thus we can use for the average velocity in this case the value v_m given by $\frac{1}{2}mv_m^2 = W$.

Substituting for this and for the value of W (continuing to neglect the difference between W and W_T), we obtain:

$$\sigma = \frac{2\pi}{3}\frac{\epsilon^2 l_0}{h}\left(\frac{3N}{\pi}\right)^{2/3} \qquad (1.11)$$

If the experimental value of $\sigma(\sim 10^5$ ohm^{-1} cm^{-1}) is substituted in 1.11 for a monovalent metal where N is about 10^{22}, it appears that l_0 is several hundred times the interatomic distance at room temperature. This is because the electrons do not collide with the atoms as such; the scattering process in a pure solid is an interaction between the electrons and the thermal vibrations of the crystal lattice. The amplitude of these vibrations is proportional to a first approximation to the absolute temperature, as a result of which l_0 is proportional to $1/T$. Thus conductivity should be proportional to $1/T$, and in a perfect lattice at rest, i.e. at zero temperature, there is no interaction and the conductivity should be infinite. In practice the deviations of the lattice from perfection due to impurities and imperfections produce a residual resistivity ρ_0 at very low temperatures, and it is the value of $(\rho - \rho_0)$ which is proportional to temperature.

5. *Thermal conductivity of Metals.* When there is a temperature gradient in a material, say in the x direction, there is a flow of heat given by $Q = -K(dT/dx)$, where K is the thermal conductivity. This

arises since at the higher temperature there is a greater energy associated with the motions of the electrons, if any are present, and in any case with the vibrations of the atoms or ions of the crystal lattice. This energy is transmitted by collisions in the former case, and by a coupling between the vibrations in the latter. It is in fact usual to treat the vibrations of the crystal lattice by a quantum-mechanical approach, and to associate them with quanta of acoustical energy called phonons, each with energy $h\nu$, where ν is the frequency of a lattice vibration. The conduction of heat by lattice vibrations can then be considered in terms of collisions between phonons, treated as particles.

In a metal the collisions between electrons are the dominating process in heat transfer and by comparison the phonon interaction can be neglected. Either case can be treated in a simple way by analogy with the well-known expression for the thermal conductivity of a population of particles as derived in the kinetic theory of gases[3].

$$K = \tfrac{1}{3}Cv\lambda \qquad \text{or} \qquad K = \tfrac{1}{3}Cv^2\tau$$

where the particles have a mean velocity v, a specific heat C at constant volume, and a mean free path λ. τ is again the mean time between collisions.

If we apply this to the electrons in a metal, or to any degenerate electron population, we have the free path l_0 as above, and the relevant velocity is again v_m.

It is not difficult to show that the mean energy E of an electron in a Fermi distribution is $\tfrac{3}{5} W$ in the first approximation. A higher approximation gives $E = \tfrac{3}{5} W\left(1 + \dfrac{5}{12}\dfrac{\pi^2 k^2 T^2}{W^2}\right)$. It follows that the specific heat per electron is

$$\frac{dE}{dT} = \frac{\pi^2 k^2 T}{2W}$$

Thus we obtain:

$$K = \frac{1}{3}\frac{N\pi^2 k^2 T v_m^2 \tau}{2W}$$
$$= \frac{1}{3}\frac{N\pi^2 k^2 T\tau}{m} = \frac{\pi^2}{3}\frac{k^2}{\epsilon^2}\sigma T \qquad (1.12)$$

This is the Wiedemann–Franz Law relating electrical and thermal conductivities for a metal, via the Lorentz number which is $\pi^2/3 \, k^2/\epsilon^2$ in this case. With K in watt/cm degree and σ in ohm^{-1} cm^{-1}, this expression becomes $K = 2\cdot4 . 10^{-8} \, \sigma T$, and K is therefore near 0·7 at room temperature for a typical metal with $\sigma = 10^5$ ohm^{-1} cm^{-1}. In pure metals, σ is approximately proportional to $1/T$ as shown above, so that K is almost independent of temperature.

6. *Electrical Conductivity of Semi-conductors.* While there is no strict definition of a semi-conductor, we are usually concerned with a material whose electrical conductivity lies between say 10^3 and 10^{-5} ohm^{-1} cm^{-1}, whereas for a metal the value is between say 10^4 and 10^6. The difference is due primarily to a lower electron concentration which occurs for reasons we shall pursue below. Frequently the electron population is less than 10^{19}/cm^3, and when this is so the considerations of p. 6 indicate that the electron population may be non-degenerate, and obey Maxwellian statistics. The case $e^{-W/kT}$ = unity occurs at room temperature (from equation 1.5) when $N = 10^{19}$, assuming the electron has its ordinary free-electron mass. We shall see later that the mass may be effectively less than this, in which case degeneracy persists to lower values of N.

In the non-degenerate case values of mean free path and mean velocity are obtained from the kinetic theory of gases, and the value of $\tau = l_0/v$ is now dependent on the electron energy and therefore on the temperature, and has the value $l_0\sqrt{(2m/\pi kT)}$. Thus the conductivity becomes

$$\sigma = \frac{2N\epsilon^2 l_0}{(2\pi mkT)^{1/2}} \quad \text{and} \quad u_0 = \frac{2\epsilon l_0}{(2\pi mkT)^{1/2}} \quad (1.13)$$

It is still true in the simplest case that l_0 is proportional to $1/T$, as a result of the lattice vibrations, and then for a non-degenerate conductor u_0 is proportional to $T^{-3/2}$. In a semi-conductor N may vary markedly with temperature as discussed below.

It should be noted that a more complex relation between u_0 and T is obtained when the electrons are scattered by the 'optical mode' lattice vibrations, compared with the above simplest case which applies to 'acoustic mode' vibrations.

If scattering occurs by charged defects or impurity atoms in the crystal lattice, the relation is different again, and in fact for this important case $u_0 \propto T^{3/2}$. This will be referred to again below. Incidentally in this case the scattering is highly anisotropic and the relaxation time is not equal to the mean time between collisions.

7. *Thermal Conductivity of Semi-conductors*. In a semi-conductor the lower electron density results in a relatively low thermal conductivity due to electrons, but now the phonon interactions with each other are larger than in a metal, and the conductivity due to phonons may be quite large.

For the electron component K_e we consider the non-degenerate case, starting again with the expression $K = \frac{1}{3}Cv\lambda = \frac{1}{3}Cv^2\tau$. The specific heat of the electrons now follows from the classical kinetic theory and is $3Nk$, while v has the value $\sqrt{(3kT/m)}$, leading to $K_e = (3Nk^2T\tau)/m$. This is again related with σ; $K_e = 3k^2\sigma T/\epsilon^2$, with a slightly modified Lorentz number compared with the degenerate case. A more rigid treatment allowing for interactions between the electrons and the vibrations of the crystal lattice (acoustic mode lattice scattering) replaces the figure 3 by 2.

The phonon contribution can be found from the same approach, making use now of the fact that the mean phonon velocity is the velocity of sound v_s in the material. Thus K_p is given by $\frac{1}{3}Cv_s\lambda$, and now the specific heat except at low temperatures has its usual value for solids $3R$, where R is the gas constant. The mean free path of the phonons varies inversely with temperature, again provided the temperature is not too low, so that $K_p = Rv_sA/T$, where A is a term independent of temperature.

As temperature falls, λ becomes limited ultimately by scattering at crystallite boundaries, and is then unaffected by further decrease of temperature. The value of C falls below $3R$ at low temperatures, and is proportional to T^3. K_p therefore follows a similar law, as v_s is only slightly temperature dependent. The resulting variations of K_p with temperature over a wide range is shown in Fig. 4.

The total thermal conductivity of a semi-conductor is $K_p + K_e$, and though K_e is less than the typical value for metals, because of the lower charge carrier density N, K_p is quite large in some materials.

Examples are 0·6 watt/cm°C at room temperature for germanium and 1·1 for silicon, with higher values for certain insulators such as sapphire and diamond.

It may be noted here that in an intrinsic semi-conductor, to be defined below, (Chapter 2, § 4), there is a third contribution to the thermal conductivity, increasing its value above $K_p + K_e$.

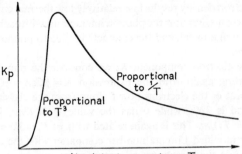

FIG. 4.—Plot of lattice thermal conductivity K_p against temperature

There may also be a contribution in any semi-conductor due to the passage of radiation through the crystal[4]. This has the magnitude

$$K_r = \frac{16n^2 \gamma T^3}{3\alpha}$$

where n is the refractive index, γ is the Stefan–Boltzmann radiation constant, and α is the absorption coefficient for the radiation, averaged over the wavelength range appropriate for the temperature T.

8. *Thermionic Emission.* We have seen that at zero temperature, a metal contains electrons with kinetic energy as large as W in Figs. 3 and 5, and that at higher temperatures a fraction of the electrons have greater energy, as in Fig. 3. At low temperatures electrons are not emitted spontaneously from solids, and we therefore know that W

in Fig. 5 is less than AO. Clearly, if an electron in the metal at zero temperature can acquire energy ϕ_0 given by $AO - W$, it may just escape, and will have zero kinetic energy on emergence. The value of

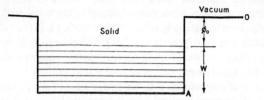

FIG. 5.—Electron levels in a solid at zero temperature

$AO - W$ at other temperatures will be described as ϕ, while ϕ_0 is the value of ϕ at absolute zero. ϕ is called the work function of the solid, and is usually measured in electron volts. When the temperature is

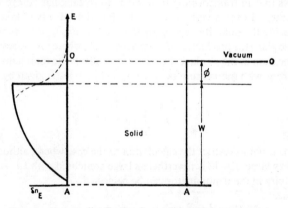

FIG. 6.—Energy distribution in a solid at high temperature.

raised, it is convenient to show in one diagram the energy distribution with the energy scale vertical, and the potential-energy diagram for a boundary between metal and a vacuum, as in Fig. 6. This involves rotating Fig. 3 to follow the convention of Figs, 1, 2, and 5, i.e., energy increasing upwards. Then the 'tail' in the distribution OP

can escape, and those electrons with kinetic energy AP will have energy OP after escape.

While, as stated above, electrons with total energy greater than AO 'may escape' it is clear that if the x direction in a three-dimensional co-ordinate system is made perpendicular to the metal surface, only those electrons will actually escape whose motion is in the x direction, and whose energy is greater than AO, and then only if there is no surface-reflection effect. We will now calculate the number of electrons which can escape from 1 cm^2 of surface at temperature T.

If the total momentum p is the vector sum of p_x, p_y and p_z, the number of electrons per cm^3 with momentum between p and $p+\delta p$ is as in 1.2.

$$\delta n_p = \frac{8\pi}{h^3} \frac{p^2 \, dp}{e^{(E-W)/kT}+1}$$

Consideration of the volume elements in a co-ordinate system shows that in transforming from polar to rectangular co-ordinates, the integral over a certain range of a function of p is obtained by replacing the quantity $4\pi p^2 \, dp$ by the product $dp_x dp_y dp_z$. Similarly, in one plane the product $dp_y \, dp_z$ replaces $2\pi r \, dr$, where r is the resultant momentum in the yz plane, i.e. $r^2 = p_y^2 + p_z^2$. Thus the total number of electrons with momentum between p_x and $p_x + \delta p_x$ is given by

$$\delta n_x = \frac{2\delta p_x}{h^3} \int_0^\infty \frac{2\pi r \, dr}{e^{(E-W)/kT}+1}$$

It is usual to restrict the calculation to the case where, although T is fairly large, $E-W$ is nevertheless large compared with kT, so that the unity in the denominator can be neglected.

Since

$$2mE = r^2 + p_x^2$$

$$\delta n_x = \frac{4\pi}{h^3} \delta p_x e^{W/kT} e^{-p_x^2/2mkT} \int_0^\infty e^{-r^2/2mkT} r \, dr$$

$$= \frac{4\pi}{h^3} e^{W/kT} mkT e^{-p^2/2mkT} \delta p_x$$

This is the number per cm^3 with momentum between p_x and $p_x + \delta p_x$, with values of resultant momentum in the yz plane over the whole range 0 to infinity.

The total number passing per second through unit area perpendicular to the x direction will be obtained by multiplying δn_x by the velocity v_x, and integrating from 0 to infinity. However, the number striking unit area of the boundary which can escape is restricted to those with momentum greater than p_a, where $p_a^2 = 2m . OA$. Thus the number escaping per unit area becomes

$$n = \frac{4\pi}{h^3} e^{W/kT} mkT \int\limits_{p_a}^{\infty} e^{-p \ /2mkT} \frac{p_x}{m} \delta p_x$$

The current is therefore

$$I = \frac{4\pi mkT}{h^3} \epsilon kT e^{W/kT} e^{-p_a^2/2mkT}$$

$$= \frac{4\pi \epsilon m k^2 T^2}{h^3} e^{-\phi/kT} = A_0 T^2 e^{-\phi/kT} \qquad (1.14)$$

The quantity $A_0 = (4\pi \epsilon m k^2)/h^3$ has the numerical value $3 \cdot 6 . 10^{11}$ when the current is measured in e.s.u., and 120 when the current is measured in amperes. This, then, is the thermionic-emission formula assuming no surface reflection. It is, of course, necessary to measure the two energies ϕ and kT in the same units. If ϕ is measured in electron volts, k must be measured similarly. It has the value $8 \cdot 62 \times 10^{-5}$ eV per degree.

It should be noted that ϕ is likely to vary with temperature, and in the simplest case the variation is linear, $\phi = \phi_0 + \alpha T$. When this applies, the thermionic emission equation becomes

$$I = \frac{4\pi \epsilon m k^2 T^2}{h^3} e^{-(\phi_0 + \alpha T)/kT}$$

$$= A_0 T^2 e^{-\alpha/k} e^{-\phi_0/kT}$$

Thus if a 'Richardson' plot is made experimentally of $\log I/T^2$ against $1/T$, the plot is linear with a slope ϕ_0, but the experimental value of A in

$$I = A T^2 e^{-\phi_0/kT} \qquad (1.15)$$

may be considerably less than A_0. The value of ϕ_0 may correspondingly differ from the photo-electric work functions which is normally measured at room temperature.

It may also be noted that image force theory shows that the potential energy of an electron in a metal changes rapidly at the surface, from its value at the level A in Figs. 2, 5 or 6 to a value $\epsilon^2/4r_0$ below the energy $A + W + \phi$. Here r_0 is a distance of the order of the interatomic spacing, and the increase by $W + \phi - \epsilon^2/4r_0$ occurs within this distance from the surface. The further increase in potential energy to the zero-level 0 then occurs according to the relation $P = -(\epsilon^2/4x)$, where x is the distance from the surface, $x > r_0$.

9. *Photo-electric Emission.* It will be clear from the discussion of Figs. 5 and 6 that a metal at the absolute zero of temperature can just liberate an electron if the electron can acquire energy equal to ϕ_0. The energy associated with light of frequency ν is $h\nu$, and incident light can therefore liberate electrons if its frequency is equal to or greater than ν_0, where in appropriate units

$$h\nu_0 = \phi_0 \qquad (1.16)$$

This gives $\nu_0 = 2 \cdot 42 . 10^{14} \phi_0 \sec^{-1}$, when ϕ_0 is measured in eV. The equivalent wavelength is $12396/\phi_0$ Ångström units.

The number of electrons liberated will be proportional to the intensity of the light at the required frequency. If the frequency is greater than ν_0, electrons can be liberated with kinetic energy greater than zero, and those which have energy near zero may include electrons from below the top of the Fermi distribution.

At higher temperatures the distribution becomes as in Fig. 6, and the thermionic emission becomes so large that the photo-electric effect is difficult to study. An intermediate temperatures where the thermionic emission is very small, the photo-emission can occur with light of frequency less than ν_0 owing to the 'tail' in the energy distribution above the Fermi level. Thus at room temperature, for example, the threshold frequency ν_0 is not sharply defined. It is likely in any case to correspond with a work function slightly different from ϕ_0, as indicated above.

10. *Adsorbed Layers.* The work function is likely to be altered if a foreign atom, ion or molecule is adsorbed at the surface of a metal.

In the extreme case for example of caesium, barium or thorium on tungsten, atoms striking the surface lose an electron to the metal, because their ionization energy is less than the work function of tungsten. The positive ions so formed are tightly bound to the metal surface, and induce a dipole layer with its positive charge outwards. This lowers the energy which the electron requires to escape, Fig. 7(b). Conversely atoms of oxygen capture electrons from the metal on

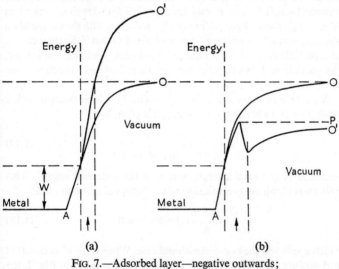

FIG. 7.—Adsorbed layer—negative outwards;
(b) Adsorbed layer—positive outwards.

impact, because of their electron affinity and so set up a dipole layer, with its negative charge outwards; this raises the work function (Fig. 7(a)). Changes in work function by more than 2 eV are produced by positive or negative ions adsorbed in this way. In such cases, the 'coverage' of the surface by the ions will be a function of temperature, so that the work function will vary with temperature much more rapidly than for a clean metal. A Richardson slope may be non-linear, or if linear over a restricted temperature range, may have an apparent 'A' value widely different from A_0.

Similar but smaller effects are produced by the adsorption of molecules with a permanent dipole, or of atoms in which dipoles are induced by the field at the surface of the metal.

11. *Potential Barriers*. In discussing Figs. 1 and 2, it was shown that the movement of a particle is restricted to a region where its total energy is greater than the potential energy of a particle in that region. When the particle, in this case the electron, is regarded as a wave pattern, there is, however, some leakage outside this region, even when $H < V$, as is shown below. Conversely, in dealing with the escape of an electron over a barrier, it was shown above (§ 8) that if the total energy of a particle is greater than the potential energy outside the barrier, the particle will escape; the wave picture, however, predicts some reflection although $H > V$.

A particle of mass m moving with velocity v is associated with a wave pattern in which the wavelength is given by:

$$\lambda = \frac{h}{mv} = \frac{h}{\sqrt{2m(H-V)}} \tag{1.17}$$

where H is the total energy, and V is the potential energy. This pattern is obtained as a solution of the Schroedinger equation:

$$\frac{d^2\psi}{dx^2} + \frac{8\pi^2 m}{h^2}(H-V)\psi = 0 \tag{1.18}$$

which applies to the one-dimensional case. When $(H-V)$ is constant and positive, as for an electron in motion in a solid as in Fig. 2, the solution is:

$$\psi = A\cos 2\pi\frac{x}{\lambda} + B\sin 2\pi\frac{x}{\lambda} \tag{1.19}$$

giving a simple sine or cosine wave pattern of wavelength

$$\frac{h}{\sqrt{2m(H-V)}}$$

The value of ψ^2 at a point then gives the probability of finding a particle at that point. This pattern will be encountered for an electron with total energy H, as long as $H > V$, which is true anywhere inside the solid for an electron with energy as at B in Fig. 2. On passing through the surface of the solid, the potential energy V becomes greater than the total energy H, for an electron such as that with total energy B. Such an electron as we saw above, § 2, cannot pass through the surface, when it is treated according to classical mechanics. However, the wave-mechanical treatment requires an investigation of the solution of equation 1.18 in the case where $V > H$. With $H - V$ constant and negative, the solution is

$$\psi = C e^{-kx} + D e^{kx} \tag{1.20}$$

where

$$k = \frac{2\pi}{h} \sqrt{2m(V-H)}$$

In this solution when x is positive, D must be zero, and ψ then decreases exponentially in the region where $V > H$. If k is large, this decrease will be rapid, but there is, nevertheless, some penetration of the quantity ψ^2 through the surface layer where $V - H$ changes sign, and therefore a finite probability of finding an electron outside the surface. For example if $V - H$ is 1 eV, the value of e^{-2kx} is of the order 10 per cent at 2·5 Ångström units outside the 'classical' boundary. This leakage of the pattern into the 'forbidden' energy zone will have applications below, and is called the 'tunnel' effect.

One application is to the case of an adsorbed layer which decreases the work function as in Fig. 7(b) in the previous section. Here the dipole layer is of molecular or atomic dimensions, and the potential hill immediately outside the surface is therefore only a few Ångström units in width. There is therefore considerable penetration, i.e., the effective work function is not reduced by the difference in level of O and P, where P is the top of the hill, but by the greater amount OO'. Only a few electrons arriving with energy between AO' and AP can, however, penetrate, the remainder being reflected. The value of the multiplying term A in equation 1.15 should therefore be less than in the case of clean surfaces. As mentioned in § 10, however, there is some doubt about the significance of A in these cases because of the variations of ϕ with temperature.

The case of the reflection of electrons with $H > V$ is not of much practical importance with a barrier following the relation $P = -\epsilon^2/4x$,

§ 9, where the reflection is not likely to exceed 10 per cent. It is of interest that the reflection of waves travelling inward towards the surface (incident electrons) should be equal to that of emerging electrons with the same total energy H.

12. *Contact Potential.* If different metals are placed in contact, the initial situation may be as in Fig. 8(a), where neither the work function ϕ nor the Fermi energy W is the same in the two metals. In the case as

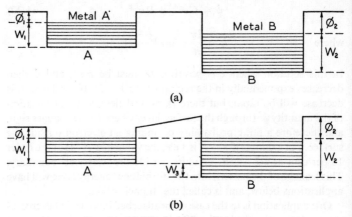

(a)

(b)

Fig. 8.—(a) Metals as brought together;
(b) Metals in contact.

drawn, there will be a tendency for electrons to escape from the left-hand metal to the right, and for a smaller number to escape from the right-hand to the left, the relative numbers depending on the two work functions ϕ_1 and ϕ_2. Thus the metal B will acquire a negative charge, and A a positive one, and a potential difference will develop between A and B. A small charge transfer is sufficient to establish a considerable potential difference. With metals the displaced charge is located at their surface. As a result of the charge transfer, the whole diagram for B will rise as in Fig. 8(b) relative to that for A. The potential difference will increase until the excess flow from left to right ceases. The net flow of electrons is now the same in each direction. Let the difference in potential energy of an electron in the two metals now be W_3. As in the previous section, the number of electrons from left to right in metal A striking unit area of the YZ plane in one second is

$$\delta n_1 \frac{p_{x1}}{m} = \frac{2}{h^3} \frac{p_{x1}}{m} \frac{\delta p_{x1} 2\pi r_1 \delta r_1}{e^{(E_1-W_1)/kT}+1} \tag{1.21}$$

The number from right to left in metal B is

$$\delta n_2 \frac{p_{x2}}{m} = \frac{2}{h^3} \frac{p_{x2}}{m} \frac{\delta p_{x2} 2\pi r_2 \delta r_2}{e^{(E_2-W_2)/kT}+1} \tag{1.22}$$

The other relations needed are

$$E_1 + W_3 = E_2, \qquad r_1 = r_2$$

$$\therefore \frac{p_{x1}^2}{2m} + W_3 = \frac{p_{x2}^2}{2m} \qquad \therefore p_{x1} \delta p_{x1} = p_{x2} \delta p_{x2}$$

Thus (1.21) becomes

$$\delta n_1 \frac{p_{x1}}{m} = \frac{2}{h^3} \frac{p_{x2}}{m} \frac{\delta p_{x2} 2\pi r_2 \delta r_2}{e^{(E_2-W_3-W_1)/kT}+1}$$

and then since $\delta n_1 \dfrac{p_{x1}}{m}$ must equal $\delta n_2 \dfrac{p_{x2}}{m}$

we have $\qquad\qquad E_2 - W_2 = E_2 - W_3 - W_1$

and therefore $\qquad\qquad W_3 = W_2 - W_1 \tag{1.23}$

This indicates that the top of the Fermi distribution at zero temperature in the two metals is at the same height. If the potential energy in B is taken for the moment as a zero level, it is clear that the potential energy to the right of B is $W_2 + \phi_2$, and that to the left of A is $W_3 + W_1 + \phi_1$. The potential difference between the metals is therefore

$$\frac{1}{\epsilon}[(W_2+\phi_2)-(W_3+W_1+\phi_1)] = \frac{1}{\epsilon}(\phi_2-\phi_1) \tag{1.24}$$

from (1.23).

If the two surfaces are separated, as for example in a vacuum tube, the exchange of electrons will be through the process of thermionic emission, and the treatment is the same as above, taking account of the electrons with energy greater than ϕ_1, ϕ_2. The same conclusion is reached, i.e. that there is a potential difference between the two surfaces given by 1.24.

It will be appreciated that if there are several metals in series, the Fermi level will be at the same height for all of them in equilibrium if they are at the same temperature, and the potential difference between two surfaces in vacuum will be determined by the work functions of those two surfaces only, independent of the intermediate metals.

REFERENCES

General References
MILLMAN, J. & SEELY, S. *Electronics*. McGraw Hill, 1951.
RAMEY, R. L. *Physical Electronics*. Prentice Hall, 1961.

(1) See for example:
   BORN, M. *Atomic Physics*. Blackie.
   MACDONALD, D. K. C., *Introductory Statistical Mechanics for Physicists*. Wiley, 1963.
   SCHRODINGER, E., *Statistical Thermodynamics*. Cambridge, 1946.
(2) See for example:
   DEKKER, A. J., *Electrical Engineering Materials*, Prentice Hall, 1959, p. 125.
   SMITH, R. A., *Semi-conductors*. Cambridge, 1959, p. 93.
(3) See for example:
   ROBERTS, J. K., & MILLER, A. R., *Heat and Thermodynamics*. Blackie, 1960, p. 285.
(4) GENZEL, L., *Zeits. Phys.* **135**, 177, 1953.

CHAPTER 2

Electrons in Crystals

Consequences of the Band Structure

1. *The Band Structure*. We wish to proceed to the case of non-metallic solids. In order to deal with these, it is necessary to consider in greater detail crystalline solids in general, including metals. This discussion will give some indication of why some solids are metals and others are not, and of the factors which determine the electrical properties of different types of solid.

The approach to the more detailed theory of the motion of electrons in solids can be made in two ways. The first is by considering what happens when an assembly of atoms, initially widely separated, is compressed until the spacing is as in the solid in question. The second is by considering the field of the array of ions in the solid, and finding the motion of electrons in this field rather than in the uniform 'smoothed-out' field, as in the previous chapter. These two methods should lead ultimately to the same general conclusions.

The first method starts with the case of two atoms. If a single atom has an outer electron in a particular energy state, and if another similar atom is brought near, the result is to form two energy levels close together, one on either side of the corresponding state for the single atom. This can be understood in an approximate manner by considering, say, the lowest energy state of a system consisting of an electron in the field of an atom core, i.e., of the ion formed by removing a valence electron from an atom. The atom core can be represented by a potential box as in Fig. 2, since energy is needed to remove an electron from the neighbourhood of the atom core, and the wave function ψ for the lowest energy state is as sketched in Fig. 9(a). Here as discussed in Chapter 1, § 11, the function in the box $(H > V)$ is a simple sine wave, and outside it $(H < V)$ the function is an exponential decay.

23

In the lowest energy state, the wavelength is the longest possible which can be associated with the box (equation 1.17) and it is found that this corresponds with fitting one half-wavelength into the box. When two boxes are placed close together, the resultant wave function is found by taking a function as in Fig. 9(a), for each box and adding these functions in the region where they overlap. If the functions in the two boxes are taken as identical (symmetrical), the result of adding them is as in Fig. 9(b). However, it is also permissible to take the sine wave in one box 180° out of phase with that in the other ('anti-symmetrical' functions), and addition in this case gives Fig. 9(c). The resultant pattern has in Fig. 9(b) a greater half-wavelength than in Fig. 9(a), while in Fig. 9(c) it is less than in Fig. 9(a). There are, there-fore, two energy states, and it is found that the separation in energy of these states increases exponentially as the boxes are brought together. A full discussion of this subject is given, for example, in reference (1) to this chapter. The two electrons are shared between the two atoms, giving a molecule in which each ψ-pattern belongs to the pair of atoms. When further atoms are added, this effect continues to occur, and in an assembly of N atoms close packed, every energy state typical of one atom is split into N states, each of which can, according to the Pauli principle, accommodate two electrons of opposite spins. The energy range covered by these levels increases exponentially as the distance between atoms decreases, as in the case of two atoms. It is not dependent on the number of atoms involved, but only on their spacing. In an assembly of N atoms, the N levels are separated so slightly that they may be regarded as an almost continuous band. In a single atom, the various energy levels are widely separated, but in the assembly of atoms comprising a solid, some of the bands formed from the various levels may remain separated, other may overlap, so that a continuous range of levels occurs. The ψ-pattern associated with levels which broaden into a band are not localized round particular atoms, but extend uniformly throughout the solid, so that the whole solid is in effect a large molecule. In finding the energy distribution of the elec-trons, the procedure is to consider the energy states available, and to allocate electrons to those states until they have all been accommo-dated, just as in finding the arrangement of the electrons in single atoms of different types in the periodic table. The inner electrons in

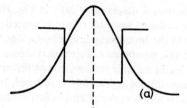

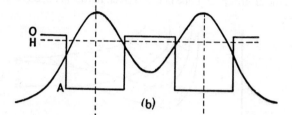

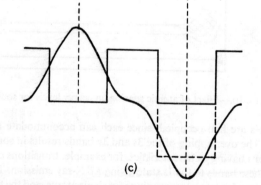

Fig. 9.—(a) Wave patterns for one atom;
(b) Symmetrical wave pattern for two close atoms;
(c) Antisymmetrical wave pattern for two close atoms.

an atom core could have their levels multiplied in the same way, but only at very close spacing, closer than in any normal solid, since the wave functions of the inner electrons are very much confined to one nuclear locality. Thus the effects on the various states for the electrons in metallic sodium are illustrated diagrammatically in Fig. 10. The levels for a single Na atom or for an assembly of widely spaced atoms are shown at the right, and the broadening into a band, due to the splitting of levels as the atomic separation r decreases, is shown to the left. r_0 is the atomic spacing in metallic sodium, and at this spacing the $1s$, $2s$, and $2p$ levels are still not appreciably broadened, but the $3s$ and $3p$ levels are considerably broadened and in fact overlap. In sodium there are two electrons per atom in the $1s$ level, two in the $2s$, six in the $2p$ group, and one in the $3s$ level. In the metal, therefore, the

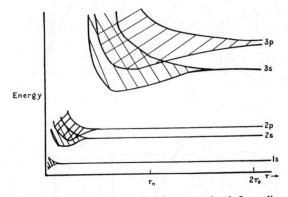

FIG. 10.—Effect of atomic spacing on energy levels for sodium

$3s$ levels are half-occupied, since each can accommodate two electrons. The overlapping of the $3s$ and $3p$ bands results in some of the electrons having p characteristics, for example, transitions can occur from these bands to the $1s$ state giving $K\beta$ X-ray emission. The selection rules of spectroscopy apply as for single atoms, and the transition from a true $3s$ level to $1s$ is forbidden. In the single unexcited atom, the $3p$ levels are unoccupied, so that the transition corresponding with $K\beta$ X-ray emission is impossible. This is one example of the difference between the electron behaviour in single atoms and in solids.

The problem of the distribution of the electrons over the closely spaced energy levels of the available bands is, in general, complicated, but in the simplest case it is similar to that of the distribution of the valence electrons in the treatment of free electrons in the previous chapter. Thus, dealing again with metallic sodium, it is necessary to consider only the $3s$ electrons, and here the lowest level in the band can accommodate two electrons, and so on as higher levels are considered, with the result that at zero temperature the distribution is the Fermi distribution again, with energy levels occupied from the bottom of the band to an energy W eV, higher, above which level no others are occupied. The value of W is given by the same expression as in the free-electron case, and the effect of temperature is also the same. The mass of the electron is, however, different from the free-electron value, as discussed below.

These conclusions apply equally to other monovalent metals; in each case the s band of the valency electrons is half-filled, there are some p characteristics, and the energy distribution is of the Fermi form, so that at zero temperature

$$\delta n_H \propto H^{1/2} \qquad (2.1)$$

where H is now the difference between the energy of the state under consideration and that at the bottom of the band. At higher temperatures δn_H depends on the Fermi probability function

$$\frac{1}{1 + e^{(E-W)/kT}}$$

and on the density of states in the band. In the simplest case this is given by the same expression as on p. 4.

In the case of a divalent metal, there are two valence electrons in the s state, thus magnesium has two $3s$ electrons. The band of s levels is therefore completely occupied. There is again overlap of the $3s$ band with higher bands, but it is of importance to consider what would happen if there was no overlap. In such a case there would be a forbidden zone between the $3s$ band and the next higher band, and it would be impossible to accelerate any $3s$ electrons by application of an electric field of normal magnitude, because there would be no levels of slightly higher energy to which the accelerated electrons could jump. Thus, although there would be many electrons in motion in the solid, none could be used for the conduction process, as only very strong fields could cause a transition to the next higher band. Similarly, ordinary temperature increases (less than 2000°) would transfer very few electrons to the next higher band unless the forbidden gap were small. In the absence of overlap, therefore, a divalent element would form an insulating solid, with its valence electrons forming a closed group. Actually overlap occurs in all the divalent elements in the solid state, and some of their valence electrons can therefore be accelerated in a moderate electric field, so that they exhibit metallic properties at all temperatures. Some of the atoms with valency four, form solids with filled bands which do not overlap,

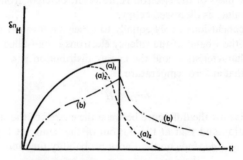

(a)₁ Half-filled band at zero temperature
(a)₂ Half-filled band at higher temperature
(b) Filled band at any temperature

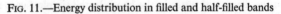

FIG. 11.—Energy distribution in filled and half-filled bands

for example, carbon in the form of diamond, and silicon and germanium which in the pure state have therefore low conductivity.

The density of states at the top of a filled band is a density of states for 'holes', see p. 33, and in the simplest case approaches the zero level in the same way as at the lower end, i.e. following a $\frac{1}{2}$-power law. Intermediately in a filled band the shape of the energy distribution curve depends on the electron wave-functions involved. The shape is indicated diagrammatically in Figs. 11 and 12, not representing any specific material.

It is important to notice that the probability of a transition from one electron state to a lower one is dependent on the number of electrons in the upper state, among other factors, and therefore the distribution curves partly determine the curves showing the intensity of the emission over the bands in the X-ray spectra already referred to. The fact that the spectra show bands is experimental confirmation of the above theory, and where the appropriate X-ray emission bands have been studied, information about the energy distribution has been deduced. When overlap of two bands of energy levels occurs, as in Fig. 12(a),

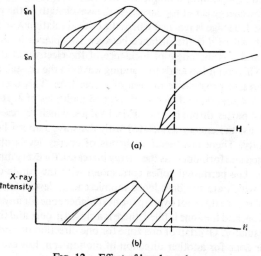

FIG. 12.—Effect of band overlap

the result is that one band will remain incompletely filled, while some of the lower energy states of the higher one are occupied. If transitions can occur from both bands to a lower level, the resultant X-ray intensity is as in Fig. 12(b). The sharp drop at the top of the bands occurs only, of course, at zero temperature, and is replaced by a 'tail' effect at higher temperatures.

The second method of considering electron motion in crystalline solids involves a study of the fitting-in of wave patterns when the potential energy is varying continuously due to the field of the atom cores.[2] The field of all the other electrons is in the first approximation smoothed out, and the field in which an electron moves is therefore strictly periodic in a perfect crystal. All the valence electrons can move continuously through the solid, since those with energy H below the zero level of the atomic potential 'boxes' (Fig. 9(b)) can leak through the barrier to the neighbouring atom, when the atomic spacing is as small as it is in the metals. (This is another example of the tunnel effect). At zero temperature in a perfect crystal, patterns can be fitted representing unhindered motion through the crystal, provided the energy is not too large. As the wavelength of the pattern is decreased, a stage is reached where the critical relation $\lambda = 2d \sin \theta$ is fulfilled, where d is the distance between two planes in the crystal lattice and θ is the angle of incidence of the electron at the lattice plane. This condition leads to standing waves in the crystal, and does not represent progressive motion of an electron. This occurs again when $2\lambda = 2d \sin \theta$, and so on for integral multiples of λ. It is found that as λ passes through these critical values, which represent Bragg reflections, the energy associated with the wave pattern has a discontinuity. There are therefore bands of energy levels alternately permitted and forbidden, as the energy increases, for every direction of motion. The permitted zones correspond with the bands discussed above, which are the broadened atomic energy levels. Clearly, if a particular zone does not overlap the next higher zone for any direction of motion, and the zone is filled, there is a closed group, and the crystal is an insulator. Overlap of one zone for one direction of motion with another zone for another direction of motion can, however, permit conductivity.

2. *Effective Mass.* The variation of total energy H with $1/\lambda$ resulting from this theory is illustrated in Fig. 13 which applies for a selected direction of motion. If the direction of motion is perpendicular to a series of planes of atoms with spacing between planes d, the discontinuities in energy occur at values of $1/\lambda = 1/2d$. For a free electron this plot would be the parabola $E = H - V = h^2/2m\lambda^2$ (equation 1.17). Notice that in this case

$$\frac{dE}{d(1/\lambda)} = \frac{h^2}{m\lambda} \quad \text{and} \quad \frac{d^2 E}{d(1/\lambda)^2} = \frac{h^2}{m} \qquad (2.2)$$

For the electrons moving in the periodic field due to a crystal lattice, the diagram shows that $d^2 H/d(1/\lambda^2)$ is not constant; its value may be taken to define an effective mass m^*, which depends on the energy of the electron and on its direction of motion in the crystal. In principle,

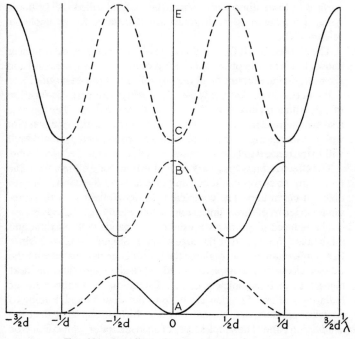

FIG. 13.—One-dimensional energy-band structure.

m^* may be higher or lower than the free-electron value at the bottom of each of the allowed bands, i.e. the shape may still be parabolic but the curvature will be less or greater than that corresponding with equation 2.2. At the top of each allowed band m^* is seen from Fig. 13 to be negative, as the curvature reverses and becomes parabolic, but concave downwards. This indicates that although $1/\lambda$ is increasing, the velocity is decreasing as the condition for a Bragg reflection is approached. At this condition, $\lambda = 2d \sin \theta$, the electron velocity is zero, as at the bottom of the band.

The value of $1/\lambda$ at which the Bragg reflection condition is encountered depends on the direction of motion and on the details of the crystal structure. For each type of crystal structure there is a surface in three dimensions where this occurs, called the Brillouin zone. The shapes of such zones are discussed, for example, in reference (3).

The allowed bands for any direction of motion will be separated as shown but it may happen that overlap occurs between one band and the next, taking account of all the possible directions of motion.

It can be shown that the value of the energy is a periodic function of $1/\lambda$, with a repetition at $1/\lambda$, $1/\lambda + 1/d$, $1/\lambda + 2/d$, etc. The figure is also symmetrical about $1/\lambda = $ zero. Thus all the information in a plot with $1/\lambda$ increasing over a wide range can be presented equally well within the range 0 to $1/2d$, as shown dotted; this is the 'reduced' zone.

The effective mass may vary with direction, for example from the minimum the curves could be parabolae in every direction, but with different curvatures. The complete behaviour might then be represented in terms of three-dimensional components m_x, m_y, m_z.

The reduced diagram gives examples of bands with maxima and minima at $1/\lambda = 0$, and at the edge of the Brillouin zone, $\lambda = 2d \sin \theta$. In a semi-conductor or insulator the lowest band associated with the valence electrons is completely filled at absolute zero, and the next highest band is completely empty. Excitation by temperature or radiation will transfer a few electrons to the second band, leading to electrical conductivity, so that this next highest band is called the conduction band. The simplest case of an insulator or semi-conductor would be when the conduction band has the form C, and the valence band the form B, i.e. the respective minimum and maximum both at $1/\lambda = 0$. Much greater complications occur however in practice; thus while the valence band usually does have its maximum at $1/\lambda = 0$ as in B, the conduction band may be quite different from C. It may also have its minimum at a zone boundary as in B, and its maximum either at zero or in an intermediate position. Thus in silicon the minima appear to lie along 100 crystallographic axes, but not at the zone boundaries, and in germanium they lie at zone boundaries in the 111 directions. In germanium moreover the maximum lies intermediately between $1/\lambda = 0$ and $1/\lambda = 1/2d$, so that there is a secondary minimum at $1/\lambda = 0$, which appears to be 0·14 eV above the main minimum.

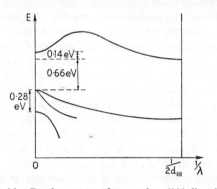

FIG. 14.—Band structure of germanium (111 direction)

(See Fig. 14). There is a complication with the valence band in Si and Ge also, in that although the maximum is at zero, there are two bands with the same maximum energy, but different curvatures.

3. *Positive Holes.* As stated above, when the temperature is above absolute zero, a few electrons are excited into the conduction band, the number depending on the temperature and on the magnitude of the forbidden energy gap. The effect on the valence band is to create a corresponding number of empty states near its top. This permits electrical (and thermal) conductivity to occur in the valence band as well as in the conduction band. The existence of the empty states permits a corresponding number of electrons to move in an applied field. There are about 10^{22} electrons/cm^3 in a valence band, and the density of vacant states will be less than this by a factor typically between 10^{10} and 10^3. The motion of electrons from occupied to unoccupied states causes the latter to change their energy. The vacant states will appear to move in the opposite direction to the main electron population and will carry a positive charge. They are therefore referred to as positive holes, and will have a charge $+\epsilon$ and an

effective mass of magnitude m_h^* corresponding with the curvature at the top of the energy bands. It will be noted that if there is a vacant energy state at a depth E below the top of the valence band, and an electron from lower in the distribution enters this state, then although it has gained energy its velocity is less, as it has come nearer to the top of the band where its velocity is zero. This is consistent with the negative mass which electrons have near the top of a band. Thus the vacant state, i.e. the hole, has now moved lower into the band, to a state with higher velocity. Thus the kinetic energy of a hole increases as its energy state moves downwards from the top of the band, so that if its energy measured downwards from a zero level at the top of the band, the effective mass of the hole is positive. The situation at the top of a filled band in terms of holes created in it is now similar, with energy measured downwards, to the situation at the bottom of an otherwise empty band when a few electrons enter it, their energy being measured upwards. This is self-consistent in view of the opposite sign of the charge.

The effective mass of holes at the top of a band may be different from that of electrons at the bottom of it, and in particular the mass of a hole at the top of a valence band is almost always different from that of an electron at the bottom of the next highest band, the conduction band. Moreover it is almost always larger, since the trend is as in Fig. 13, for band width and curvature to increase the higher the band. The separation between bands tends also to decrease. The condition as in silicon and germanium where two bands coincide at the top of the valence bands means that two types of hole can exist, with different masses.

4. *Types of Semi-conductor*. An important class of materials with non-overlapping bands is formed by the elements and compounds with covalent bonds between the atoms in the crystal lattice. Here each atom has four nearest neighbours, and provides one electron to the bond with each of those neighbours, i.e. each atom provides four electrons in all to the bonds, and each bond is formed by two electrons. Examples are the 4-valent elements; diamond, silicon, germanium and the grey form of tin. Each of these are insulators at absolute zero, and have conductivity at higher temperatures in so far

as electrons and/or holes are formed by rise of temperature or some other mechanism. Other examples are provided by the compound between elements in column three and those in column five of the periodic table, e.g. indium antimonide, gallium arsenide, aluminium phosphide, etc. Here the crystal lattice is similar, and there are covalent bonds each with two electrons. The fact that there are two kinds of atom with different electron affinity leads to the charge distribution between the atoms being somewhat unsymmetrical in these compounds, whereas it is symmetrical in the elements. This distortion of the covalent bonds is equivalent to there being a small ionic component in the bonding in these compounds.

The fully ionic bond is illustrated in the Group I–Group VII compounds, the alkali halides, e.g. NaCl. Here the outer s electrons are lost from the metal atom and are almost completely localized at the negative ion, where they complete the stable, inert-gas eight-electron shell. The negative ion therefore has its valence electron bands fully occupied. Thus in NaCl the sodium $3s$ band is unoccupied, and the chlorine $3s$ and $3p$ bands are both filled, so that the crystal is an insulator at low temperatures. Moreover the energy gap is large, i.e. the $3s$ band is several electron volts higher than the next lowest filled band, so that the material has very low electron conductivity at high temperatures also (in fact ionic conductivity develops as temperature rises before the electron conductivity is appreciable). The spacing between like ions, e.g. between Na^+ and Na^+ or between Cl^- and Cl^-, is of course greater than the lattice spacing, and is considerably greater than the spacing between Na ions in sodium metal, thus the broadening of the s levels is less marked than in the metal, and the forbidden gaps are larger.

There is a similar situation with the Group II–Group VI compounds, e.g. MgO and ZnS, in that again at $0°K$ the negative ion bands are filled and the metal ion band which is the next highest is empty. These materials are also insulators therefore at $0°K$ but the forbidden energy gaps are lower in some of them than in the alkali halides. The II–VI compounds are by no means fully ionic however, i.e. it is not true that two electrons from each metal atom go over to the non-metallic ions to complete their stable octet. There is some degree of charge sharing, i.e. of covalency in the bond.

If the width of the forbidden band is Q eV, it is shown below that the number of electrons per cm^3 excited to the conduction band by temperature alone is about $n_R = 10^{19} e^{-Q/2kT_R}$ at room temperature T_R. This is well below 10^{19} unless Q is of the same order as kT_R, i.e. $\frac{1}{40}$ eV. The ionic solids and others with Q greater than 3 eV are insulators at this temperature when pure and in the absence of excitation by radiation. With silicon, $Q = 1 \cdot 1$ eV, leading to $n_R \sim 10^{10}/cm^3$, and with germanium $Q = 0 \cdot 66$ eV, $n_R \sim 2 \cdot 10^{13}$. These electron densities are much less than in a metal, but do lead to appreciable conductivity. Materials which give conductivity in the range say 10^{-5} to 10^3 ohm^{-1} cm^{-1} at room temperature when pure and not excited by radiation are called intrinsic semi-conductors.

5. *Effects of Impurities*. If we consider a covalent-bonded crystal such as silicon or germanium, we see that if a 5-valent impurity atom is substituted for one of the parent atoms of the lattice, it becomes bonded to its neighbours by four of its electrons, leaving one electron only loosely bonded to the impurity atom. If such impurity atoms are far apart, their electron orbitals will not overlap, and the 'extra' electrons will occupy a single energy level. At high impurity density this level will be broadened into a band by interaction between neighbours just as with the levels of the silicon or germanium atoms. We shall consider only the non-overlapping case. The 'extra' electron is bound to the remainder of the impurity atom by forces resembling those in a hydrogen atom, except that the crystal lattice has a dielectric constant different from unity. This is because the whole of the inner-shell 4-valence electron structure acts as a single positive charge relative to the one loosely bound electron. If the calculations for the Bohr orbits of a hydrogen atom are carried out for a medium of dielectric constant K, it is seen that the forces between the inner structure and the electron are multiplied by $1/K$, the energy separation between levels by $1/K^2$, and the radius of the electron orbital by K. Account should also be taken of the value of the effective mass of the electron, arising from its motion in the periodic crystal lattice. Using m_e for Ge $= 0 \cdot 2m$, $K = 16$, the 'ionization' energy for such an impurity atom in Ge will be about $(13 \cdot 6 \cdot 0 \cdot 2)/16^2 = 0 \cdot 01$ eV. Thus at absolute zero the impurity atoms will have all five electrons

bound to them, but at higher temperatures the fifth electron will be readily excited above its ground state to excited states, and still at a low temperature it will become 'ionized', i.e. free from the impurity atom and mobile in the crystal lattice. It must now in effect have entered the 'conduction band', since it is free to move in an applied field. This means that the ground state for the fifth electron is about 0·01 eV below the bottom of the conduction band. Evidently each impurity atom can release one electron into the conduction band when an energy 0·01 eV is available thermally. The semi-conductor is now of the 'extrinsic' type, and the case considered is of 'donor' impurities and the crystal becomes an n-type semi-conductor, n because the carrier of charge is negative.

It should be appreciated that the valence electrons forming the covalent bond are at all times in rapid motion, exchanging position with each other. When the pattern is complete, i.e. at absolute zero when there are two electrons in each of the bonds, no electrical conduction can be produced by these electrons, in spite of their rapid motion. This is because these electrons have all the energy values available to them, i.e. they form the filled valence band already discussed. The extra electrons provided by donor atoms, however, can move in the crystal independently of the localized bonds, so that there is a spatial distinction between the two types of electrons. The same applies to electrons excited to the conduction band by radiation or by increase of temperature.

If a 3-valent impurity is substituted for a parent atom, there is now one electron missing in the bonding scheme at the impurity site at absolute zero. When the temperature rises, a neighbouring electron may enter this bond, leaving the 'missing' site in an adjacent position. This is equivalent to the motion of a hole in the valence band, and if we pursue the analogy, we find that the hole is loosely bound to the impurity atom, that it is present there at absolute zero, and that the bonding energy is that between a positive charge moving in the field of a negative charge in a dielectric medium. Thus the same approximation can be made, and again low binding energy is found, for example about 0·01 eV in germanium.

The ground state level for the hole attached to the impurity atom is now represented by a level a little above the top of the valence band.

Since the diagram must be thought of in an inverted form for holes, increase of temperature excites holes into states of higher energy, i.e. downwards into the valence band. This is quite equivalent to stating that the ground state levels are empty of electrons at $0°K$ (full of holes) and that raising the temperature excites electrons from the top of the valence band to the ground state levels, so creating holes in the valence band. The impurity atoms are therefore called in this case 'acceptors', and the semi-conductor is p-type, positive charge carriers.

When donors are present, the electron density n_e at low temperatures will be greater than its intrinsic value, because the separation R between the donor level and the conduction band is much less than Q. The density of donor atoms is much less than that of the ions of the crystal, however, so that at sufficiently high temperatures the intrinsic value of n_e will become greater than that due to the donor centres. The temperature where this happens will be higher, the higher the value of Q. If during increase of temperature the stage is reached where all the donor atoms are ionized, there will be no further increase in n_e with temperature below the intrinsic range, and n_e is independent of temperature. The temperature range over which the density of electrons due to donor atoms is greater than the intrinsic density is called the extrinsic range, and where it is independent of temperature, the exhaustion range.

Thus the possible types of curve for a solid containing donor impurities are as in Fig. 15. At high temperatures the intrinsic behaviour occurs, and the plot of $\log n_e$ against $1/T$ is nearly linear with a slope near $Q/2$. At very low temperatures the plot of $\log n_e$ due to donor impurities has much lower slope near $R/2$. Curve A shows an impurity which is not fully ionized at the temperature where the intrinsic electron density becomes of the same order of magnitude as the extrinsic density. In B, C and D there are increasing amounts of impurity atoms, which in C are fully ionized to the left of the point G.

In a p-type semi-conductor, the same considerations apply if we consider the density of holes n_h instead of the electron density, and the dependence of n_h on the density of acceptor centres. When the material becomes fully intrinsic the densities of electrons and holes become equal, in accordance with the definition of the intrinsic behaviour, so that the same plot applies in Fig. 15 for the intrinsic range. In both cases of course the variation of electrical conductivity with temperature depends on that of the carrier density (electrons or holes) and also on that of the mobility (Chapter 3, § 2).

It will be evident that impurities which behave in the above way have a profound effect on the electrical properties. Thus if there is one part in a million of phosphorus or arsenic in germanium or silicon,

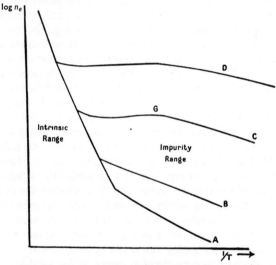

FIG. 15.—Typical relations between conductivity and temperature in semi-conductors

the corresponding number of electrons, about 10^{16} is freed into the conduction band at quite low temperatures (below $100°$K). This electron density remains constant over the exhaustion range, and is larger than the intrinsic density at room temperature. Boron or aluminium would provide a corresponding density of holes.

The effects described will be more complicated if the impurity atom can donate or accept more than one electron. This subject will not be pursued here, though it is important in connection with electron 'trapping' and recombination processes.

4

The impurities mentioned above enter the lattice substitutionally, i.e. each atom at a crystal lattice site in place of a parent atom. This is possible provided the parent and impurity atoms are not too different in size. In some types of crystal there are spaces in the lattice into which interstitial atoms can move. These may be atoms of an impurity, or parent atoms may be displaced from their 'correct' position into interstitial sites.

The behaviour is more complicated in compounds than in the covalent elements. For example the effect of an impurity atom depends on which atom it replaces. In a III–V compound, a group VI impurity will act as a donor if it substitutes for a Group V atom, and a Group IV atom as an acceptor. Replacing a Group III atom however, a Group IV atom is a donor and a group II an acceptor. The effects can be deduced for II–VI compounds in a similar way. Apart from impurities, during the formation or heat treatment of compounds it is possible for: (i) some ions of the lattice to move from lattice points to interstitial positions, forming vacant lattice points, without any impurity or stoichiometric excess of one ion over the other in the solid as a whole (ii) ions of the two types to evaporate unequally, forming a stoichiometric excess of one, leading to conductivity as below. (iii) When ions of one type evaporate more than another, the excess of the ions remaining may continue situated at lattice points, or may go into interstitial positions. (iv) When vacancies have been formed, foreign ions may occupy these sites, if their size is suitable. In cases (ii) and (iii) the evaporating atoms will be neutral, and changes in electron distribution may therefore occur in the solid. Thus if a negative ion leaves a lattice point, it may evaporate as an atom, leaving an electron at the vacant point. This will not be stationary, but will move in the field of the positive charge corresponding with the missing ion, forming a system like a hydrogen atom but with energies modified by the term $1/K^2$ as above. This system can be ionized with sufficient energy, and therefore is equivalent to a donor impurity atom. Similarly, an excess vacancy in the positive-ion lattice, i.e. a vacancy which is not balanced electrically by a corresponding negative-ion vacancy, can act as an acceptor centre. If there are equal numbers of vacancies of the two types, there may be equal numbers of sites which are not individually neutralized in this way. A vacant negative-ion site which has no electron is clearly a centre of attraction which can act as a 'trap', holding an electron which was in motion and which passes near enough. An actual crystal may possess centres of various types, and the behaviour will then be correspondingly complex.

Trapping can clearly occur at a negative-ion site where the ion is missing, or at a negative ion which has lost an electron due to the interaction with particles or radiation incident on the solid. In addition, however, it appears that an insulating crystal contains many trapping centres due solely to lattice distortions. The number of these can be reduced by annealing, and carefully annealed single crystals can be obtained almost free from such traps. Trapping on crystal surfaces is referred to below (Chapter 2, § 7 and Chapter 5).

One example of the effect of ion vacancies is provided by the alkali halides, e.g. NaCl. A typical crystal contains an equal number of vacancies in both ion sites, the number being a function of the temperature and the previous history. If the crystal is heated in Na vapour, Cl atoms evaporate, and electrons enter and take the place of the Cl ions, while positive Na ions enter and fill the appropriate vacancies. The electrons and Na ions originate in the Na atoms striking the crystal surface. Thus the number of Cl deficiencies increases relative to the Na, and the number of electrons found at negative sites also increases. This alters the optical properties of the crystal, causing absorption bands in the visible part of the spectrum, so that the electrons bound at the negative-ion sites are called 'colour centres'. There is not, however, appreciable electronic conductivity at room temperature, since the ground state for the bound electron is more than 1 eV below the conduction band. Another example is zinc oxide, which loses oxygen when heated in vacuum. The excess zinc ions in this case do not stay at their original sites, but move into interstitial positions, and two electrons are transferred to these ions. At least one of these is loosely bound, and the system is easily ionized, thus the reduced oxide is a good semi-conductor.

It is found generally that if one ion in an ionic crystal has more than one possible valency, as in the case of Zn, semi-conducting properties are readily developed. For example, in ZnO and TiO_2, the cation is not in its lowest possible valence state. Heating in oxygen has no effect, but on heating in H_2 or in vacuum, reduction occurs easily, and as there are large interstitial spaces in the lattice of these oxides, the excess cations move into these positions, and act as donor centres, since they have gained electrons in the reduction process. In the converse case where the cation is in its lowest valence state, e.g. Cu^+ in Cu_2O, or Ni^{++} in NiO, reduction does not occur readily, but heating in oxygen causes formation of cation vacancies. When a cation escapes from the crystal, it takes an electron with it, so that an electron deficiency or positive hole is formed, leading to p-type conductivity. This hole will occur in the negative-ion band if this is the highest filled band, as would be true in the alkali halides or in the simple divalent oxides or sulphides. In Cu_2O, however, the highest filled band is the Cu^+ band, not the oxygen band, and the hole is created in the Cu^+ band, i.e. the escaping electron is provided by a Cu^+ ion, converting it to a cupric Cu^{++} ion. There is here no question of ions moving to interstitial positions.

6. *Nickel Oxide.* In some materials there is very little overlap of the electron orbitals between the nearest neighbours of like type of ion, so that there is no broad band of energy levels associated with electrons originating from these ions. This is unlike the situation in most of the semi-conductors mentioned so far. When there is little overlap the electrons are trapped most of the time in the neighbourhood of the ions from which they originate. There is a possibility however of 'hopping' from one site to another, which becomes greater as temperature rises. Thus there is a small conductivity when a field is applied, due to a small mobility which rises with temperature. The electronic component of the thermal conductivity is thought to be zero in these materials.

The best known example of this 'narrow band' type of semi-conductor is perhaps nickel oxide NiO, which has been studied in some detail. It is an insulator in its stoichiometric form NiO. Although the oxygen ions form a closed shell by taking two electrons from the nickel atoms, the latter have a partly filled $3d$ band, with eight electrons per atom where ten can be accommodated. Thus if there was appreciable overlap between the $3d$ orbitals, unfilled bands would be formed and conductivity would occur. This does not happen however. Heating in oxygen produces nickel ion vacancies, and the composition $Ni_{(1-x)}O$, where x is usually below 1 per cent, and represents the fraction of missing nickel ions. The x nickel ion vacancies result in the formation of $2x$ Ni^{3+} ions, to maintain electrical neutrality in the crystal. The extra positive charge can move from one Ni^{2+} to another, so leading to p-type electrical conductivity. However there is no valence band for the holes involved, which need thermal activation to hop from one site to the next. The conductivity depends on the value of x, the frequency of vibration of the ions of the crystal lattice, the activation energy for the hopping process, and the temperature. Such a semi-conductor is not very useful because the value of x will vary with temperature and with the oxygen pressure in the ambient atmosphere.

A better way of producing Ni^{3+} ions in NiO is to replace some of the Ni by an ion of lower valency, and moreover of fixed valency, such as Li. Each Li ion replacing Ni^{2+} leads to the formation of a Ni^{3+} ion to give charge neutrality; the composition is now $Li_xNi_{(1-x)}O$ and x is now equal to the Ni^{3+} concentration. However x can now reach values of 10–20 per cent, and is then not dependent on oxygen vapour pressure, since it is much larger than the highest value of x which oxygen atmospheres can produce at ordinary pressures. With $x = 0.1$, the electrical conductivity at room temperature is about 1 ohm^{-1} cm^{-1}, at least 10^{10} times higher than for stoichiometric NiO.

Many other types of compound behave in this way, when they contain an ion with more than one valency. Examples are the perovskite structure, spinels, tungstates, and titanium dioxide and various titanates. It is of course necessary that there should be a fixed-valence ion which will substitute for the mixed-valence ion; Li^+ substitutes for Ni^{2+} because the ions are very similar in size.

As a result of the hopping process the effective mobility in these compounds may be considerably less than unity, compared with several thousand in broad-band semi-conductors.

7. *Multi-crystalline Solids*. It is necessary to point out that the above discussion has been concerned with the properties of a crystal lattice, and starting with the case of a perfect lattice, has proceeded to deal with the effect of impurities in the lattice, and lattice defects of various

TABLE 1

	Melting Point °C	Dielectric Constant	Energy Gap eV	Mobility Room Temp.		Effective Mass		Thermal Conductivity W/cm degree
				Electrons cm²/volt sec	Holes	Electrons m_e/m	Holes m_h/m	
Diamond	3500		5·2	1800	1200			2
Silicon	1420	12	1·2	1300	500	0·25	0·4	1·1
Germanium	958	16	0·67	3800	1800	0·2	0·4	0·6
Grey Tin	232		0·08	2000	1000			
InSb	527	16	0·18	80000	800	0·013	0·18	0·15
InAs	942	12	0·36	30000	250	0·03	0·15	0·3
InP	1070	9	1·3	4000	200	0·08		
GaSb	705	14	0·7	5000	1000	0·05		
GaAs	1280	11	1·35	5000	400			0·27
GaP	1350	9	2·2	110	80			0·3
AlSb	1050	9	1·5	450	150		0·4	0·5
SiC		10	2·8	220	48	0·72	1	
HgTe	670		<0	24000		0·03		
HgSe	690		<0	10000		0·05		0·02
CdTe	1040	11	1·5	600	50			

CdSe	1250		1·7	200			0·5	
CdS	1475	12	2·4	200	20	0·13	0·7	
ZnS	1850	8	3·6	1000		0·2	1·8	
ZnO		85	3·2	300				
PbTe	904		0·25	900	300	0·38		0·023
PbSe	1065		0·22	600	500	0·3		
PbS	1110	70	0·3		400	0·15		
ZnTe			2·3					
ZnSb			0·56		300	0·15		
CdSb	770		0·48		500			
Mg_2Sn	1150		0·33	300	250			
Mg_2Ge	1100		0·74	280	110			
Mg_2Si	1120		0·77	400	60			
Ca_2Sn	920		0·9					
Ca_2Si			1·9					
Cu_2O			1·9					
Bi_2Te_3	575	85	0·15	420	50			0·016
Bi_2Se_3	706		0·27	600	400			0·05
Sb_2Te_3	620				300			
Sb_2Se_3	617		1·2	100				
Ga_2Te_3	793		1·3					
In_2Te_3	667		1·0					
$CuInSe_2$	990		0·9	1000	50			
$AgFeSe_2$	737		0·23	300	70			0·03

types. The discussion has referred, therefore, basically to a single crystal, and has not included the properties of the polycrystalline solid. If we extend the scope of the discussion, we find that the grain boundaries in a solid may be important in several respects; thus they will tend to increase electron and phonon scattering and therefore electrical and thermal resistivity; foreign atoms may become included in grain boundaries, and in semi-conductors may modify the behaviour in a manner discussed in Chapter 5, where adsorbed atoms are discussed and shown to create space-charge zones near the crystal boundaries; while, in the absence of adsorbed atoms, crystal surfaces are places where charge can accumulate (surface states, Chapter 5). This last effect is of importance, for example, in considering conductivity induced in an insulator or high-resistance semi-conductor by radiation or electron bombardment – the crystal surfaces are places where trapping of photo-electrons can occur, so limiting their range of movement in an applied field. In the case of a porous substance formed by compression or partial sintering of a powder, the above effects are exaggerated, and the d.c. conductivity may be determined almost entirely by point contacts between the particles of the powder, which are themselves usually crystal aggregates.

8. *Applications – Thermistors.* The high temperature-coefficient of resistance associated with some types of semi-conductor, especially those with a 'hopping' mechanism, has clearly considerable practical importance in connection with measuring and controlling temperature. Semi-conductors developed and manufactured for these purposes form *therm*ally sensitive res*istors*, and are frequently referred to as thermistors. They can be made very compactly as small beads, discs, or flakes, with small heat capacity, and will therefore give high sensitivity and rapid response. It is necessary of course, for usefulness in industry that samples should be reproducible, should retain constant characteristics in use, should be rugged, and that the contacts should be reliable. The reproducibility has been the greatest difficulty: clearly when conductivity and its temperature coefficient are influenced by less than one part in a million of impurity, control is very impracticable. The best results are therefore obtained with one of the groups of compounds which are not highly sensitive to impurities,

e.g., (a) Fe_3O_4 and the corresponding spinels, or (b) sintered mixtures of NiO, Mn_2O_3, and Co_2O_3. Reproducible results can also be obtained using (c) TiO_2, which is reduced in hydrogen or vacuum to give the 'blue' form which is an n-type semi-conductor. It is simpler to control the reduction to obtain a desired result if the powdered TiO_2 is first mixed with MgO, and treated as a ceramic; the final product here appears to be a compound of the two oxides. In addition to resistance thermometers and bolometers, thermistors have found a variety of less obvious applications as discussed, for example, in reference (4) to this chapter.

REFERENCES

General References

AZAROFF, L. V., *Introduction to Solids*. McGraw Hill, 1960.

CUSACK, N., *The Electrical and Magnetic Properties of Solids*. Longmans.

DUNLAP, W. C., *An Introduction to Semi-conductors*. Wiley, 1957.

HANNAY, N. B., *Semi-conductors*. Reinhold, 1959.

HILSUM, C., & ROSE-INNES, A. C., *Semi-conducting IV-V Compounds*. Pergamon. 1960.

HUME-ROTHERY, W., *Atomic Theory for Students of Metallurgy*. Institute of Metals. 1946.

KITTEL, C., *Introduction to Solid State Physics*. Wiley, 1956.

MOTT, N. F., & GURNEY, R. W., *Electronic Processes in Ionic Crystals*. Oxford, 1948.

SHOCKLEY, W., *Electrons and Holes in Semi-conductors*. Van Nostrand 1950.

SINNOTT, M. S., *The Solid State for Engineers*. Wiley, 1958.

SMITH, R. A., *Semi-conductors*. Cambridge, 1959.

WILSON, A. H., *Semi-conductors and Metals*. Cambridge, 1959.

VAN DER ZIEL, A., *Solid State Physical Electronics*. Macmillan, 1958.

MOTT, N. F., & JONES, H., *Theory of Properties of Metals and Alloys*. Dover, 1958.

(1) GURNEY, R. W., *Elementary Quantum Mechanics*. Cambridge, 1940.

(2) BLOCH, F., *Zeits. Phys.* **52**, 555, 1928.
   WILSON, A. H., *The Theory of Metals*. Cambridge, 1953.

(3) BRILLOUIN, L., *Quantenstatistik*. Springer–Berlin. 1931.
   SEITZ, F., *Modern Theory of Solids*. McGraw Hill, 1940.

(4) BECKER, J. A., GREEN, C. B., & PEARSON, G. L., *Elec. Eng.* **65**, 711, 1946.

CHAPTER 3

Carrier Density and Conductivity in Semi-Conductors

1. *Carrier Density.* An intrinsic semi-conductor at low temperatures will have a few electrons in the conduction band, and an equal number of holes in the highest filled band. If there are no impurity levels, and if the energy gap between the two bands is Q as in Fig. 16, the number of electrons in the upper band per unit volume is

$$n = 2\frac{(2\pi kT)^{3/2}}{h^3}(m_e m_h)^{3/4}e^{-Q/2kT} \tag{3.1}$$

$$= 5\cdot10^{15}\cdot\left(\frac{m_e m_h}{m^2}\right)^{3/4} T^{3/2}e^{-Q/2kT} \tag{3.2}$$

Here m_e is the density-of-states effective mass of the electrons, and m_h that of the holes; m is the free-electron mass. When there is a single maximum or minimum at $1/\lambda = $ zero, and when the effective mass is isotropic, these values are the same as m^*, which was defined in terms of the band structure on p. 31. When the effective mass is anisotropic m_e and m_h have mean values derived from the components m_x, m_y, m_z. When there are N equivalent minima the density-of-states effective mass is $N^{2/3}$ times the value associated with one minimum.

Expression 3.1 results from the following considerations.

Suppose the Fermi level in the semi-conductor is at an energy W referred to the bottom of the conduction band. A negative value of W indicates a Fermi level below the zero level at the bottom of the conduction band, and conversely, a positive value indicates a Fermi level above the zero level. Let the density of states in the lower part

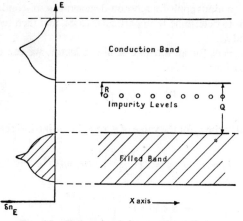

FIG. 16.—Energy levels in a semi-conductor

of the conduction band be given by $s_e \delta E$. Then the total number of electrons in the conduction band at temperature T is

$$\int_0^\infty \frac{2s_e \delta E}{1 + e^{(E-W)/kT}}$$

The number of holes in the valence band is

$$\int_0^\infty \frac{2s_h \delta E}{1 + e^{(W-E)/Tk}}$$

where s_h is the density of states for holes.

If W is less than $-kT$ the integrals can be evaluated neglecting the unity in the denominators. When the density of states has the value given on p. 4, the result is:

$$n_e = 2\left(\frac{2\pi m_e kT}{h^2}\right)^{3/2} e^{W/kT} = N_{ce} e^{W/kT} \qquad (3.3)$$

$$n_h = 2\left(\frac{2\pi m_h kT}{h^2}\right)^{3/2} e^{-(W+Q)/kT} = N_{ch} e^{-(W+Q)/kT} \qquad (3.4)$$

These equations apply for any non-degenerate semi-conductor. The problem is to determine W in particular cases, and then substitute to find n_e and n_h.

Since $n_e = n_h$ for an intrinsic semi-conductor, we can equate 3.3 and 3.4, giving:

$$W = -Q/2 + \frac{3kT}{4} \ln \frac{m_h}{m_e} \qquad (3.5)$$

We shall write n_i for the value of n_e or n_h in the intrinsic case, so that

$$n_i = n_e = n_h = 2 \left(\frac{2\pi kT}{h^2} \right)^{3/2} (m_e m_h)^{3/4} e^{-Q/2kT}$$

$$= 5 \times 10^{15} \, T^{3/2} \left(\frac{m_e m_h}{m^2} \right)^{3/4} e^{-Q/2kT}$$

as in (3.2).

If W/kT is not less than -1, the full expressions for n_e and n_h must be integrated. This involves the use of numerical methods to determine

$$\int_0^\infty \frac{(E/kT)^{1/2} \, d(E/kT)}{1 + \exp(E/kT - W/kT)}$$

which is written as $F_{1/2}(W/kT)$. In other parts of the theory of electrons in solids, similar integrals are encountered but with powers in the numerator other than $1/2$. These Fermi integrals have been tabulated by McDougall and Stoner.[1] When the expression is as above, the value of n_e falls below that given by equation 3.3 when $W/kT > -1$, and $\ln(n_e/N_{ce})$ falls below the value W/kT. With $W/kT > 5$, $F_{1/2}(W/kT) \sim 2/3(W/kT)^{3/2}$, and the relation between n_e and W becomes as in equation 1.3. The semi-conductor is then fully degenerate. It is partially degenerate between $W/kT = -1$ and $W/kT = 5$.

Similarly the hole density is now given by

$$n_h = \frac{2N_{ch}}{\sqrt{\pi}} F_{1/2} \left[-\frac{(W+Q)}{kT} \right],$$

and the value of W is obtained by equating this with

$$n_e = \frac{2N_{ce}}{\sqrt{\pi}} F_{1/2}\left[\frac{W}{kT}\right]$$

Notice that from 3.3 and 3.4, the product $n_e n_h$ is given by

$$n_e n_h = N_{ce} N_{ch} e^{-Q/kT} \qquad (3.6)$$

This product is independent of W, and in the intrinsic case is equal to n_i^2. However, 3.6 as well as 3.3 and 3.4 will apply for all non-degenerate semi-conductors, i.e. if n_e is made unequal to n_h by 'doping' the semi-conductor with impurity (extrinsic case see below) equation 3.6 will still apply.

On introducing donor levels at a depth R below the conduction band (Fig. 16) by any of the mechanisms discussed above, e.g. impurity centres or lattice vacancies, if the density of centres is n_0/cm^3, the number of electrons in the conduction band when the temperature is low and when n is small compared with n_0 is

$$n = (2) n_0^{1/2} \frac{(2\pi m_e kT)^{3/4}}{h^{3/2}} e^{-R/2kT} \qquad (3.7)\dagger$$

$$= (2) n_0^{1/2} \times 5 \times 10^7 \left(\frac{m_e}{m}\right)^{3/4} T^{3/4} \times e^{-R/2kT} \qquad (3.8)\dagger$$

This expression is obtained by determining as before the position of the Fermi level of the semi-conductor relative to the bottom of the conduction band, but now we approximate by neglecting the holes.

At absolute zero all the donor atoms have their extra electrons bound to them, in their lowest energy state, at energy R below the conduction band. The total density of states associated with these atoms is therefore equal to their density, i.e. n_0/cm^3. At a higher temperature the probability of occupancy is $f = 1/[1 + e^{(-R-W)/kT}]$, so that the density of electrons still attached to the donor atoms is $N_d = n_0/[1 + e^{(-R-W)/kT}]$. The density of electrons in the conduction band is given as before by $N_{ce} e^{W/kT}$, and is equal to $n_0 - N_d$. We have therefore an equation for W as required.

† The factor 2 will appear only in the unlikely case of an impurity occupied by 2 electrons of opposite spin.

The complete equation is

$$n_e + N_{ce}\mathrm{e}^{-R/kT} = \frac{n_0 N_{ce}}{n_e}\mathrm{e}^{-R/kT}$$

If $N_{ce}\mathrm{e}^{-R/kT}$ is small compared with n_e, which requires low temperatures such that the Fermi level is higher than the impurity level, this gives

$$n_e = \sqrt{N_{ce}n_0}\,\mathrm{e}^{-R/2kT} \qquad (3.9)$$

and

$$W = -R/2 + \frac{kT}{2}\ln\frac{n_0}{N_{ce}} \qquad (3.10)$$

(3.9) should be reduced by the factor $\sqrt{2}$ to allow for the normal situation that an impurity level can accommodate one electron of either spin. This will give agreement with (3.7) omitting the (2). With paired spins, (3.9) must be multiplied by $\sqrt{2}$.

When the temperature is such that the Fermi level is below the impurity levels, $\mathrm{e}^{(-R-W)/kT}$ is large and N_d is much less than n_0. Then $n_e \sim n_0$, and the donor centres are 'fully ionized'; increase of temperature cannot increase n_e while the semi-conductor remains extrinsic. We now have $n_e = n_0 = N_{ce}\mathrm{e}^{W/kT}$

$$\therefore W = kT\ln\left(\frac{n_0}{N_{ce}}\right) \qquad (3.11)$$

This applies provided that $n_0 \ll N_{ce}$. As temperature rises, N_{ce} rises, so that the Fermi level falls further below the impurity levels, until finally it reaches the intrinsic level (3.5). Similar formulae apply for p-type semi-conductors, replacing m_e by m_h and N_{ce} by N_{ch}, and W^1, the height above the valence band.

The intrinsic density of holes and electrons at room temperature given (equation 3.1) is about $2 \cdot 10^{13}/\mathrm{cm}^3$ for germanium and about $10^{10}/\mathrm{cm}^3$ for silicon. An impurity density of 10^{16} atoms/cm^3, i.e. less than one part per million, can therefore raise the carrier density at room temperature (impurities fully ionized) by factors of 10^3 and 10^6 respectively. This illustrates the very important effect of trace impurities in semi-conductors. Their technology depends on obtaining desired impurities at levels usually between $\frac{1}{10}$ and 10 parts per million, and on lowering the concentration of undesired impurities below $\frac{1}{10}$ part per million. The desired impurities must also have an accurately controlled distribution, in the crystals of material. In order to avoid complications due to grain boundaries and internal surfaces, such as those mentioned in Chapter 2, § 7, semi-conductors are usually required in the form of single crystals.

2. *Conductivity.* The conductivity σ due to a density of carriers n per cm^3 is given by $\sigma = neu_0$, where u_0 is the mobility, defined and discussed in § 1.4 and § 1.6. It was shown in § 1.6 that when a semiconductor has a non-degenerate electron and hole population, and when the charge carriers are scattered by acoustic mode lattice vibrations, $u_0 \propto T^{-3/2}$. It is clear therefore from 3.1 or 3.2 that in the

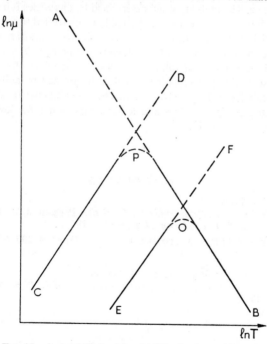

Fig. 17.—ln (mobility) against ln T for lattice and inpurity scattering

intrinsic case σ is proportional to $e^{-Q/2kT}$, since the $T^{-3/2}$ in u_0 cancels with the $T^{3/2}$ in 3.1.

In the extrinsic case however, under the same conditions, the carrier density is constant in the exhaustion range, and over that temperature range therefore $\sigma \propto T^{-3/2}$. Thus here, unlike the intrinsic case, the conductivity falls as temperature rises.

It is important however to recall (§ 1.6) that when electrons are scattered by ionized impurity atoms, $u_0 \propto T^{3/2}$. Thus if $\ln u_0$ is plotted against ln (temperature), there will be a set of limiting values determined by lattice scattering, AB in Fig. 17, and sets where the limiting value is determined by impurity scattering such as CD, EF etc., where CD corresponds to a low density of impurity atoms, and EF to a higher one. The mobility when determined by impurities is inversely proportional to their density, and directly proportional to the square of the dielectric constant. The net effect of the two types of scattering must be to produce a mobility following the plots CPB and EOB, determined by the lower value. (The net relaxation time τ for a number of scattering processes in parallel is determined by adding the reciprocals $1/\tau = (1/\tau_1) + (1/\tau_2) + \ldots$). Thus the plot changes slope at O, P, etc., at higher values and lower temperatures the lower the impurity concentration.

REFERENCES

General References
BLAKEMORE, J. S., *Semi-conductor Statistics*. Pergamon, 1961.
SMITH, R. A., *Semi-conductors*. Cambridge, 1959.

(1) MCDOUGALL, J., & STONER, E. C., *Phil. Trans. A.* **237**, 67, 1938.

See also

RHODES, P., *Proc. Roy. Soc. A.* **204**, 396, 1950.
BEER, A. C., CHASE, M. N., & CHOQUARD, P. E., *Helv. Phys. Acta.* **28**, 529, 1955.

CHAPTER 4

Hall Effect, Magneto Resistance and Thermoelectric Properties

1. *Hall Effect.* Measurement of the Hall effect is a very important source of information about semi-conductors. If a current I amp. flows uniformly through a solid, and a magnetic field H oersteds is applied perpendicular to the direction of current flow, then a voltage gradient can be detected in the third direction at right angles to the other two. This is because the electrons tend to travel in curved paths in the magnetic field, and a space charge is formed along the sides of the conductor due to the change in balance of the electron concentration. This space charge causes the build up of a transverse electric field until in equilibrium the electrons travel without deflection under the combined influence of the magnetic field and this transverse electric field. The Hall coefficient R is the potential gradient produced by unit applied magnetic field when unit current density flows through the specimen.

If the electrons in the solid are regarded as completely free, then, when the current density is i and the applied field is H, the transverse force on one of the electrons due to the electric field is $RiH\epsilon$. The opposing force due to the magnetic field is given by $H\epsilon u$, where u is the mean drift velocity of the electrons. Now the current density i is also given by $n\epsilon u$, where n is the electron density, thus equating the two forces gives

$$Ri\epsilon H = Rnu\epsilon^2 H = H\epsilon u$$

$$\therefore R = \frac{1}{n\epsilon} \tag{4.1}$$

A detailed theory for the case of a non-degenerate semi-conductor, taking into account the electron velocity distribution, gives the slightly different result $R = 3\pi/8n\epsilon$, while the result $R = 1/n\epsilon$ applies for a metal or degenerate semi-conductor. In each case the direction of the gradient R depends on the sign of the charge of the carriers of the current, thus if the carriers are predominantly positive holes, the gradient is in the opposite direction to that when the carriers are

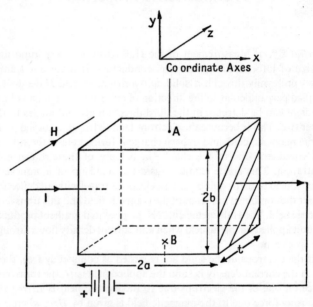

FIG. 18.—Hall effect in a solid

predominantly electrons. In experiments on the Hall effect, it is convenient to work with a rectangular specimen, with contacts over the end surfaces, and potential measuring probes arranged centrally in the sides, as in Fig. 18.

Consider a rectangular block of material as in Fig. 18, of length $2a$, breadth $2b$, and thickness t in the z direction. The current I flows in the

x direction, the field H is applied in the z direction, and the transverse e.m.f. is therefore created in the y direction. The current density is $i = I/2bt$, and if R is measured in cm^3 per coulomb, the Hall potential gradient is given by $10^{-8} R.i.H$ volts/cm. Thus the voltage between A and B is given by

$$V_{AB} = \frac{10^{-8} 2b . RHi}{2bt} = 10^{-8} \frac{RHI}{t} \qquad (4.2)$$

In this expression, since R is measured in terms of coulombs, its value $R = 1/n\epsilon$ (or $R = 3\pi/8n\epsilon$ when non-degenerate) is obtained by taking the value of ϵ in coulombs, i.e. $1\cdot6.10^{-19}$. When electrons are the predominant carriers, A is negative with respect to B in Fig. 18, and conversely in the case of an excess of holes (p-type). If experiments give the magnitude and sign of the voltage between A and B, the value of R from (4.2) gives the number of carriers

$$n = \frac{1}{R\epsilon} \quad \text{or} \quad n = \frac{3\pi}{8\epsilon R} = \frac{7\cdot4.10^{18}}{R}$$

and the sign of these carriers. If the conductivity is also known, $\sigma = n\epsilon u_0$ and $u_0 = \sigma/n\epsilon = R\sigma$, in the degenerate case

or $$u_0 = \frac{\sigma}{n\epsilon} = \frac{8\sigma R}{3\pi} = 0\cdot85 R\sigma, \text{ non-degenerate} \qquad (4.3)$$

Thus the mobility can be found from R and σ. Some values of u_0 are shown in Table 1. It may be remarked that in the sample the length a should be at least four times as great as b in order that equation 4.2 shall lead to an accurate estimate of R.[1]

It may be noted that the relation $R = (3\pi/8 \; 1/n\epsilon)$ for a non-degenerate semi-conductor applies only when the energy band structure has the simple form of curves B and C, Fig. 13, and when the predominant scattering mechanism is lattice scattering. An appreciable degree of impurity scattering raises R above the value $3\pi/8n\epsilon$, while a band structure with multiple minima, e.g. Fig. 14, can raise or lower R according to the magnitudes of the effective masses of the electron for different crystallographic directions.

In an intrinsic semi-conductor the number of electrons is equal to the number of holes, and if each had the same mobility, the Hall effect would be zero. In practice, the mobility is usually different, that of the electron being larger, so that there is a Hall effect indicating an n-type behaviour, though the value of n deduced from R in this case has no significance unless the mobility ratio is large. The expression for R in this case is

$$R = \frac{3\pi}{8\epsilon} \frac{n_1 C^2 - n_2}{(n_1 C + n_2)^2} \tag{4.4}$$

where n_1 is the electron density, n_2 the hole density, and C the ratio of electron-to-hole mobility.

It will be noted that when an n-type semi-conductor goes over to an intrinsic type as temperature is raised, the Hall coefficient R will fall continuously, while σ rises continuously. When, however, a p-type conductor goes to intrinsic, R passes through zero when $n_1 C^2 = n_2$, since the sign changes at the transition, thus there is a discontinuity in a plot of the log of the numerical value of R against $1/T$, but not in that of $\log \sigma$. If a homogeneous semi-conductor contains both donor and acceptor centres, there may be a reversal of sign of the Hall effect on raising the temperature while still within the extrinsic range. This possibility depends on the relative concentrations and activation energies of the two types of centre.

2. *Magneto Resistance*. When a magnetic field is applied transversely, e.g. in the z direction, the conductivity in the x direction may be altered. With an intrinsic semi-conductor there is an increase in resistivity $\Delta\rho$ proportional to H^2, $(\Delta\rho/\rho_0) = M_i H^2$, where M_i depends on the electron and hole mobilities and densities. With an extrinsic non-degenerate semi-conductor, with a simple energy band structure there is an increase $(\Delta\rho/\rho_0) = M_e R_0^2 \sigma_0^2 H^2$, where σ_0 is the zero-field conductivity, ρ_0 the zero-field resistivity, and R_0 the low-field Hall coefficient. M_e is 0.275 for acoustic mode lattice scattering, and 0.57 for impurity scattering. The relationship between $\Delta\rho$ and H^2 is linear only at low fields; the resistivity saturates at high fields at a multiple of ρ_0 depending again on the scattering law. There is no increase in resistivity with field in a degenerate extrinsic semi-conductor.

When the energy bands are multiple or non-spherical, more complex results are obtained, as for example with germanium and silicon.[2]

3. *Thermoelectric Effects.* It is shown in Chapter 5 that when a metal and a semi-conductor are in contact, their Fermi Levels are at the same height. In the semi-conductor the Fermi level is at a height W above the bottom of the conduction band. The value of W was calculated in Chapter 3 for intrinsic and for extrinsic n-type semi-conductors, and was shown to be negative in intrinsic semi-conductors (unless Q and m_e/m_h are very small), and in non-degenerate extrinsic

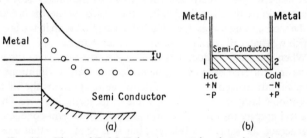

FIG. 19.—Thermal E. M. F. between metal and semi-conductor

semi-conductors. In such cases the bottom of the conduction band is higher in energy than the Fermi levels in the metal and semi-conductor.

Consider specifically such an n-type extrinsic semi-conductor (Fig. 19). At absolute zero it would be necessary to provide the energy $UeV = -W$ to raise an electron from the top of the Fermi distribution in the metal to the bottom of the conduction band in the semi-conductor. At higher temperatures, if the semi-conductor is non-degenerate, the electrons in the conduction band have a mean energy $3kT/2$. There is now a tail on the energy distribution of the electrons in the metal, and those with sufficient energy are able to cross the junction into the conduction band. Each electron which does so extracts energy from the metal, producing a cooling of the junction. The simple approach we have made so far would predict the magnitude of this energy to be $U + 3/2kT$. The situation is in fact quite analogous to thermionic emission; U corresponds with the work function ϕ for emission into a vacuum. An extension of the treatment in Chapter 1 shows that the energy which has to be provided to evaporate an electron is $\phi + 2kT$, not $\phi + 3/2kT$,[3] and correspondingly a more correct expression in the present case is $U + 2kT$.

In general the Peltier coefficient for a junction between two materials is defined as π, such that the heat generated or extracted at the junction for a current I is $Q = \pi I$. In our case we have therefore $\pi = 1/\epsilon(U + 2kT)$, since $U + 2kT$ is the energy associated with the transfer of one electron across the junction. By convention the sign is negative in this case.

A more sophisticated treatment shows that the energy generation or extraction depends on the details of the electron scattering processes in the semi-conductor, as a result of which the first term in the bracket which we shall call A may have values other than 2.

When the semi-conductor is non-degenerate, and when the electrons are scattered primarily by acoustic-mode lattice vibrations in a covalent lattice such as silicon or germanium, A retains the value 2. In an ionic lattice A would be 3, while if the scattering were wholly due to impurity ions the value would be 4. If the semi-conductor is degenerate, the value of A is larger, but W is positive so that π is less than for a non-degenerate semi-conductor. The argument is the same for an extrinsic p-type semi-conductor, referring to the transfer of a hole from the semi-conductor to the metal. The mathematics is the same except that the sign is reversed, i.e. $\pi = +(1/\epsilon)(AkT - W')$, indicating a heating effect when holes pass from semi-conductor to metal. Here W' is the depth of the Fermi level below the top of the valence band. In the non-degenerate case this is a negative quantity. In an intrinsic semi-conductor the effects due to holes and to electrons are in opposition, and the Peltier coefficient is correspondingly small. It is in fact zero if the effective masses of electrons and holes are equal, and if the scattering mechanism is the same for holes and for electrons.

The Seebeck coefficient, or thermoelectric power, is given by $\alpha = \pi/T$, and is therefore $-(k/\epsilon)[A - (W/kT)]$ for electrons passing from metal to n-type semi-conductor, and $+k/\epsilon[A - (W'/kT)]$ for holes passing from p-type semi-conductor to metal. The signs are such that the hot junction is positive in an n-type semi-conductor.

It should be noted that according to equation 3.3, which applies for any type of non-degenerate semi-conductor, $W/kT = \ln n_e/N_{ce}$. Thus for an extrinsic n-type semi-conductor

$$\alpha = \frac{\pi}{T} = -\frac{k}{\epsilon}\left(A - \ln\frac{n_e}{N_{ce}}\right) \qquad (4.5)$$

If m_e is known, i.e. the density of states effective mass, and if A is known, measurement of α gives the value of n_e.

Since k/ϵ is $86 \cdot 2\ \mu$ volts per degree, and since A is equal to or greater than 2 for non-generate semi-conductors, it is evident that for such materials α is greater than 170 μV/°C, depending on the magnitude of $-W/kT$. This is in contrast with values of a few tens of μV/°C for junctions between two metals.

It may be noted that the above expressions may not apply at very low temperatures. The temperature gradient in a solid implies a gradient of amplitude of lattice vibrations, and therefore a gradient of the effectiveness with which electrons are scattered by these vibrations. This causes the electrons to be in effect pushed towards the cold end, and to be present in excess there, so increasing the charge on the cold junction, i.e., raising the thermo-electric power. This effect is called 'phonon drag', because electrons are dragged by the lattice vibrations, which are represented in a quantum treatment by the particles called phonons.[4] The effect is not appreciable in semi-conductors with high carrier densities, or with low thermal conductivity, or at high temperatures. It is present in high-purity germanium and silicon below 200° K, and in diamond below 100° C.

4. *Electrolytic Conductivity*. It is necessary to point out that in ionic solids at the higher temperatures, electrolytic conductivity can occur, and the variation of conductivity with temperature is exponential, so that confusion can occur as to whether ions or electrons are the source of an observed conductivity. The ionic conductivity may be due to the presence either of interstitial ions or of lattice vacancies. If an interstitial ion gains enough energy, it may move to another interstitial position, while when a vacancy occurs, a neighbouring ion may gain enough energy to move it into the vacancy. There is thus a random movement at sufficient temperature, which leads to diffusion

if there is a concentration gradient, or to current flow in an applied field. The ion flow in an applied field leads to charge accumulation at the electrodes and polarization, which is one method of distinguishing ion and electron conduction. Another difference is that the Hall effect is too small to measure with ionic conduction because of the very low mobility. This is also true however in semi-conductors such as NiO (Chapter 2, § 6).

5. *Applications*. The Hall effect in a semi-conductor is of great importance in view of the information it gives about carrier density and mobility. In addition it has several interesting applications. One example is to the measurement of magnetic field. High resistance germanium, for example with resistivity greater than 1 ohm cm has a small number of carriers n, of the order of 10^{15}/cm^3, and therefore a large Hall coefficient, of the order 10^4. This is so large that it is possible to obtain Hall e.m.f.s of the order 1 microvolt per gauss, with a current of 1 mA, through a small specimen of thickness of the order 1 mm. Thus, for measurement of inductions of a few hundred or thousand gauss, ordinary portable d.c. instruments can be used, and a compact unit can be made which will give a continuous record of field strength. The Ge specimen can be small so that local variations in field strength can be explored.

Another application of the Hall effect is to analogue multiplication. The Hall voltage is obtained by multiplying the current through the specimen by the applied magnetic field, which can be controlled by the magnitude of the current through field coils. Thus the output voltage is dependent on the product of the two currents.

A related application is to the measurement of power in an electromagnetic field, since the current in the sample depends on the electric field and the Hall voltage depends on the magnetic field and the current. The Hall effect is independent of frequency to very high frequencies, so that both these methods can be used at microwave frequencies.

It should be noted that if the contacts A and B are incorrectly positioned, there will be a voltage difference between them (Fig. 18) in the absence of a magnetic field, with magnitude depending on the geometry and on the voltage V between the ends of the specimen.

This out of balance voltage can be compensated, but clearly this may become difficult in a high resistance specimen which would have high values of V for a given current. In fact the usefulness as a device depends on the ratio of the Hall voltage V^H (which is proportional to R.H.I.), to the applied voltage V. Since $V \propto I/\sigma$, V_H/V is proportional to $R\sigma$, which is proportional to the mobility u_0. Thus useful performance is obtained if u_0 is large, so that n-type germanium, indium arsenide and indium antimonide are the most satisfactory materials.

Thermo-junctions between different metals have been used for a long time for temperature measurement. With such junctions the Seebeck coefficient is too small to give a useful source of power, and correspondingly the Peltier coefficient is too small to use the cold junction for refrigeration. With semi-conductors however much larger effects can be obtained. Unfortunately numerically large values of α or π are obtained only when W is much less than $-kT$, which corresponds with a low carrier density and a low electrical conductivity. This is of course associated with large Joule heating losses in the semi-conductor, which lower the efficiency for thermo-electric generation or refrigeration. It is found that the performance depends on the quantity $z = \alpha^2 \sigma/K$ where K is the thermal conductivity, and that $\alpha^2 \sigma$ is a maximum for any material when its impurity density is such that W is near zero. The value of α is then Ak/e, which is 173 μV/$^\circ$C when $A = 2$. The establishment of W determines the carrier density at a given temperature, and a material is therefore needed with as high a value of σ as possible for a given carrier density, i.e. a high mobility. Clearly a low value of K is also necessary.

Semi-conducting compounds with high atomic weight have so far been found to give the highest values of z at room temperature, in particular bismuth telluride Bi_2Te_3 and lead telluride $PbTe$. With both of these, improvement is obtained by partial substitution by elements from the same column of the periodic table, i.e. $(Bi-Sb)_2Te_3$ and Pb_2TeSe. The former alloys give values of z near $3 \cdot 10^{-3}$ at room temperature, and the latter near $2 \cdot 10^{-3}$. A junction between n and p-type alloys of the bismuth antimony telluride type is useful for refrigeration, and will produce a temperature drop below room temperature of 70°C or more. The efficiency is less than that of a conventional refrigerator for powers of a few hundred watts, but the latter is not efficient at low powers, and cannot be scaled down in size. Thermo-electric refrigeration is therefore very valuable for a variety of types of small unit, with cooling powers of a few watts or a few tens of watts.

Bi_2Te_3 and $(Bi–Sb)_2Te_3$ cannot be used above about 150°C, since their energy gap is small (0·15 eV) and α starts to fall due to intrinsic behaviour at that temperature. PbTe although poorer at room temperature, has a larger energy gap and can be used to 500°C. It is therefore useful for thermo-electric generation. GeTe alloyed with a small proportion of Bi_2Te_3 can also be used (p-type) between 400 and 500°C. With a hot junction near 500°C and a cold junction near 0°C, PbTe and GeTe thermo-junctions generate electricity (d.c.) directly from heat with an efficiency of about 5 per cent.

Recently it has been shown (5) that alloys of PbTe with $AgSbTe_2$ have values of z of $2·10^{-3}$ at temperatures near 700°C. These are therefore the best materials so far for thermo-electric generation. Again the performance is poor compared with conventional methods of generating power, but compact, silent units can be made with no moving parts and therefore no wear, which are useful as small power units in portable equipment and installations in remote places where infrequent servicing is available.

REFERENCES

General References

DRABBLE, J. R., & GOLDSMID, H. J., *Thermal Conduction in Semiconductors*. Pergamon, 1961.

GOLDSMID, H. J., *Application of Thermoelectricity*. Methuen, 1960.

HEIKES, R. R., & URE, R. W., *Thermoelectricity, Science and Engineering*. Interscience, 1961.

IOFFE, A. F., & STILBANS, L. S. *Physical Problems of Thermoelectricity*. Repts. on Progress in Physics XXII. Phys. Soc. 1959.

IOFFE, A. F., *Semi-conductor Elements and Thermoelectric Cooling*. Infosearch, 1957.

PUTLEY, E. H., *The Hall Effect and Related Phenomena*, Butterworth, 1960.

WRIGHT, D. A., *Brit. Journ. App. Phys.* **15**, 217, 1964.

GOLDSMID, H. J., *Thermoelectric Refrigeration*, Heywood, 1964.

(1) ISENBERG, I., RUSSELL, B. R., & GREESE, R. F., *Rev. Sci. Inst.* **19**, 685, 1948.
(2) SMITH, R. A., *Semi-conductors*. Cambridge, 1959, p. 127, 361.
(3) See for example:
MILLMAN, J., & SEELY, S., *Electronics*. McGraw Hill, Chapter V.
RAMEY, R. L., *Physical Electronics*. Prentice-Hall, 1961, Chapter 5.
(4) HERRING, C., *Phys. Rev.* **96**, 1163, 1954.
(5) FLEISCHMANN, H., LUY, H., & RUPPRECHT, J., *Z. Naturforsch.* **18a**, 646, 1963.

CHAPTER 5

Surface Properties

1. *Surfaces and Surface States.* The argument leading to the band structure and the diagrams such as Fig. 11, 12, 13 and 15 was based on the interaction between electrons and a periodic crystal lattice. It is evident that at a surface, i.e. the boundary of such a periodic lattice, the situation may be more complex. In effect the sequence of allowed and forbidden energy states breaks down at the surface, and energy states may be occupied there which would be forbidden within the crystal. This applies to both electrons and holes. The occupancy of these states at the surface leads to a layer of surface charge, to the production of a space-charge zone beneath the surface, and to the establishment of a surface potential different from that in the interior.

In the simplest case we can consider a semi-conductor which is *n*-type, and which has a rather large energy gap so that we can completely neglect the behaviour of holes. We then suppose that at the surface some of the surface states, e.g. N_s/cm^2, are occupied by electrons. To maintain charge neutrality, there must be a corresponding number of electrons missing in the bulk of the semi-conductor just beneath the surface. If the depth affected is d, and the density of donor centres present is n_0/cm^3, then each centre to a depth d will have lost its electron, with $n_0 d = N_s$. In the space-charge region between $x = 0$ and $x = d$ (Fig. 20) the potential has the value V which is zero at $x = d$, and V_0 at $x = 0$. Then Poisson's equation gives

$$\frac{d^2 V}{dx^2} = \frac{4\pi n_0 \epsilon}{K}$$

where K is the dielectric constant.

66

At $x = 0$, dV/dx and V equal zero, so that

$$V_0 = \frac{2\pi n_0 \epsilon d^2}{K} = \frac{2\pi \epsilon N_s d}{K} \qquad (5.1)$$

Similar effects will result from the adsorption of atoms, ions or molecules with a large electron affinity. It will be noted that whereas on a metal, adsorbed layers can produce a dipole layer where the separation between the charges is of atomic dimensions, with the

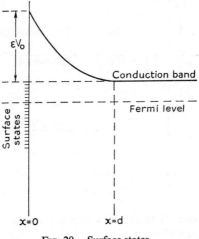

FIG. 20.—Surface states

semi-conductor d may be quite large. Thus n_0 is typically between 10^{14} and $10^{19}/\text{cm}^3$, and N_s may be 10^{12}–$10^{14}/\text{cm}^2$.

If the energy gap is smaller, or if the semi-conductor is more nearly intrinsic, the behaviour of the valence band near the surface becomes important. Thus if as in Fig. 21 the valence band comes nearer to the Fermi level than the conduction band as the surface is approached, there is a p-type layer immediately below the surface, with a hole density depending on the separation in energy h between the valence band and the Fermi level. This is called an inversion layer. The expressions for V_0 and d are now more complicated.

If surface states or adsorbed layers are present which can give up electrons to the crystal, a negative space charge will be formed causing a downward curvature of the bands on approaching the surface. It then becomes possible to form an *n*-type inversion layer on a *p*-type semi-conductor. Changes in ambient atmosphere or in a

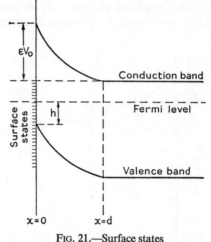

FIG. 21.—Surface states

surrounding electrolyte can thus produce a range of effects at a semi-conductor surface.

It should be noted that in the above we have had in mind a 'clean' semi-conductor surface. This is very difficult to attain in practice, and under normal conditions an oxide layer is present at the surface of semi-conductors such as germanium and silicon. There are then surface states at the outer surface of the oxide layer, with a density in the range 10^{13}–10^{15}/cm^2, but there are usually states present at the inner boundary between the oxide and the semi-conductor, with a lower density. The time constant for charge sharing with the outer surface is long compared with that for the inner surface or for a clean surface.

When extra carriers of either sign are formed near a surface, e.g.

by incident radiation or particles, the existence of surface states may increase the rate of recombination of electrons and holes above the value typical of the bulk of the solid. Extra holes are accelerated to the surface when the field is as shown in Fig. 21, and will recombine rapidly with the electrons in the surface states which are responsible for the internal field. Conversely, if holes are trapped at the surface, the energy levels are bent in the opposite way to that shown in Fig. 21, and electrons in the crystal are accelerated to the surface, where they will recombine with the trapped holes. The surface recombination

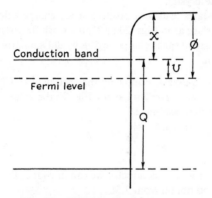

Fig. 22.—Thermionic work function

rate is minimized when the levels are horizontal as in Fig. 22. It is sometimes possible to achieve this condition by control of the environment.

2. *Work Function.* If a semi-conductor had no surface states, the potential energy diagram at the surface would be as in Fig. 22. If we take the zero of energy at the bottom of the conduction band, then the Fermi level is at a height W above it, and if W is negative, the electron gas in the conduction band will be non-degenerate if $W < -2kT$. This was the situation to which equations 3.5, 3.9 and 3.10 applied. We shall write here $W = -U$, $U > 2kT$. The Fermi level is the energy at which the probability of occupation is $\frac{1}{2}$, and the

electron distribution is determined by multiplying the Fermi probability function by the density of states (cf. pp. 4, 49). The energy distribution of the electrons in the conduction band is thus determined by the position of the Fermi level, and if we calculate the thermionic emission by following the procedure in Chapter 1, it is clear that the thermionic work function will have the value $\phi = \chi - W = \chi + U$. Here χ is the energy separation between the bottom of the conduction band and the potential energy of an electron outside and remote from the surface. χ is called the electron affinity of the crystal.

If surface states lead to a positive space charge below the semiconductor surface as in Figs. 20 or 21, the work function is increased by ϵV_0. A negative space charge region would similarly decrease the work function.

3. *Thermionic Emission.* Following the argument of Chapter 1, it is clear that the energy $pa^2/2m$ has for Fig. 22 the value χ, so that the emission equation becomes:

$$I = \frac{4\pi \epsilon m_e k^2 T^2}{h^3} \, e^{-(\chi - W)/kT} = A_0 T^2 e^{-\phi/kT} \qquad (5.2)$$

as for a metal.

For an intrinsic semi-conductor we can introduce the height of the Fermi level and obtain from 3.5:

$$I = \frac{4\pi \epsilon m_e k^2 T^2}{h^3} \left(\frac{m_h}{m_e}\right)^{3/4} e^{-[\chi + (Q/2)]/kT} \qquad (5.3)$$

Similarly for an n-type extrinsic non-degenerate semi-conductor with its donor centres partly ionized we can substitute in 5.2 from (3.10), giving:

$$I = \frac{4\pi \epsilon m_e k^2 T^2}{h^3} \frac{h^{3/2} n_0^{1/2}}{(2\pi m_e kT)^{3/4}} e^{-[\chi + (R/2)]/kT}$$

$$= \frac{\epsilon n_0^{1/2} \pi^{1/4} m_e^{1/4} (2kT)^{5/4}}{h^{3/2}} e^{-[\chi + (R/2)]/kT} \qquad (5.4)$$

When fully ionized we can substitute from 3.11 giving:

$$I = n_0 \epsilon \sqrt{\left(\frac{kT}{2\pi m_e}\right)} e^{-\chi/kT} \qquad (5.5)$$

In fact when the semi-conductor is non-degenerate, we have from 1.5, (or 3.3)

$$e^{W/kT} = \frac{n_e h^3}{2(2\pi m_e kT)^{3/2}}$$

where n_e is the density of electrons in the conduction band. Thus in this case:

$$I = \frac{4\pi\epsilon m_e k^2 T^2}{h^3} \frac{n_e h^3}{2(2\pi m_e kT)^{3/2}} e^{-\chi/kT}$$

$$= n_e \epsilon \sqrt{\left(\frac{kT}{2\pi m_e}\right)} e^{-\chi/kT} \tag{5.6}$$

Thus 5.5 is a special case of 5.6.

Under the conditions of 5.6, it may be noted that since $\sigma = n_e \epsilon u_0$,

$$I/\sigma = \frac{1}{u_0} \sqrt{\left(\frac{kT}{2\pi m_e}\right)} e^{-\chi/kT} \tag{5.7}$$

Thus the correlation between thermionic emission and electrical conductivity for a semi-conductor can give an experimental value of χ, if u_0 is known. u_0 may of course be determined from a Hall effect experiment.

Values of χ are 1 eV or less for the alkali halides and caesium antimonide, of the order 1 eV for BaO, SrO and CaO and ThO_2, and higher for most other semi-conductors and insulators, e.g. at least 4 eV for Ge and Si.

Surface states will modify the value of χ as above by the amount ϵV_0 which can be determined if n_0 and N_s are known.

4. *Contacts.* If a semi-conductor is placed in contact with a metal, the argument used in Chapter 1 shows that in thermal equilibrium the Fermi levels must be at the same height in the metal and semi-conductor, just as in the case of two metals. Charge will be transferred until this situation is established, leading to the presence of a dipole layer at the interface. This is normally associated with a space charge layer below the semi-conductor surface, e.g. if the work function of the metal were the greater, the energy levels at the contact would be

6

as in Fig. 23 for a strongly n-type semi-conductor with a large energy gap. The energy increase through the space charge region is again given by $\epsilon V_0 = (2\pi n_0 \epsilon^2 d^2)/K$.

If no surface states were present, i.e. if the levels at the surface of the semi-conductor in isolation were as in Fig. 22, then the energy ϵV_0 would be equal to the difference between the two work functions, $\phi_{\text{metal}} - \phi_{\text{semi-conductor}}$. When surface states are present and occupied however, the metal may be brought into contact with very little effect on the values of V_0 and d which are typical of the semi-conductor in

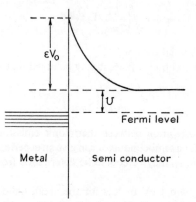

FIG. 23.—Metal–semi-conductor contact

isolation. Thus the value of V_0 is often insensitive in practice to the values of the work functions.

If a voltage is applied across the contact such that the semi-conductor becomes more positive, the balance between the flow of electrons in the two directions across the contact will be disturbed and a net current will flow. The resistance of the space charge region will be much greater than that across the remainder of the semi-conductor or the metal, and most of the total volt drop will be that across the space charge. A positive voltage V applied to the semi-conductor will give a total volt drop $V + V_0$ across this region, so that

$$2\pi n_0 \epsilon d^2 = K(V + V_0).$$

The thickness of the space charge region is increased, and there is a small out of balance electron flow from metal to semi-conductor. If however the voltage on the semi-conductor is negative, the levels in the semi-conductor are raised and d decreases, becoming zero when $V = V_0$. There is therefore a decrease in barrier height for electrons flowing from semi-conductor to metal, and a marked increase in the net flow in this direction. Thus the contact produces a rectifier action.

The electron current from metal to semi-conductor is determined by the barrier height $\epsilon Vo + U$, and is proportional to $e^{-(\epsilon V_0 + U)/kT}$. We shall call this current $I_0 = A e^{-(\epsilon V_0 + U)/kT}$. With zero applied voltage the current in the opposite direction is the same. When the applied voltage is V, the barrier height is altered as discussed above and the current from semi-conductor to metal becomes $I_0 e^{-\epsilon V/kT}$. The net current is therefore $I = I_0(1 - e^{-\epsilon V/kT})$.

If the space charge layer is rather thin, such that collisions can be neglected during the electron motion through it, then 'diode theory' applies and the value of A follows from 5.6 above, $A = n\epsilon \sqrt{(kT/2\pi m)}$. In practice this rarely applies, partly because collisions do occur. Also, when the semi-conductor is negative, holes can flow into it from the metal, and if an inversion layer is present (Fig. 21) this flow may be large and the contact 'injects holes'. Correspondingly if the semi-conductor is p-type with bands bent downwards, the forward current may be associated with electron injection. In each case the reverse direction of bending gives little rectification.

In practice moreover if a metal is brought into contact with a semi-conductor, both surfaces may have oxide layers present which will increase the total thickness of the high resistivity region and complicate the situation further. Thus the behaviour of such contacts is complex and in addition they are usually found to be unstable. The more successful procedures for stabilizing them involve a heating process which leads to alloying between metal and semi-conductor, and to a final situation involving p–n junctions, which are discussed below.

In point-contact rectifiers there is usually a lack of geometrical symmetry, in that one metal contact to the semi-conductor is of very small area, and the other relatively large. In addition the method of preparation usually produces an electrical asymmetry, in that the object is to make the large-area contact 'ohmic', i.e. a contact which does not rectify and which produces a minimum disturbance in electron or hole concentrations in its vicinity. In large-area contact rectifiers there may be geometrical symmetry, and the rectification of the complete device depends wholly on the lack of electrical symmetry. Thus in the copper oxide and selenium rectifiers, the semi-conductor makes a 'good' contact to a metal electrode on one surface, but a relatively insulating layer is present between the metal and semi-conductor at the other surface.

5. *The Franck–Condon Principle.* In dealing with the band theory of solids, the analogy was made between the solid and a giant molecule. All the above considerations of band widths and band separations, of electron populations in a conduction band, of thermionic emission and contact potential, have assumed thermal equilibrium throughout the system, and statistical methods applicable to a state of thermal equilibrium were used in deriving equations 3.1, 3.7, 3.9. The values of R or Q appearing in these equations and in 5.3 and 5.4 refer therefore to transitions occurring while thermal equilibrium is maintained. However, when an electron transition from one energy state to another occurs as a result of incident radiation, the transition occurs so rapidly that thermal equilibrium is not established. The solid as a whole will be disturbed by the transition, and after it has occurred there will be slight movements of ions to new positions representing a minimum potential energy of the 'molecule' in its new state. The initial electron transition is therefore, in general, a transition to an energy state higher than that represented by thermal equilibrium under the new conditions. The energy required to transfer an electron from the valence band or from an impurity level to the conduction band when the electrons are excited by radiation may therefore be greater than the value of Q or R which is applicable in the above equations. Q and R are thermal activation energies, which may be less than the corresponding optical excitation energies. This conclusion is a development of the Franck–Condon principle, which states that when electron transitions occur in simple molecules, there is no relative motion of the atoms concerned until after the electron transition is complete.

The difference between optical and thermal activation energies depends on the polarization mechanism in the crystal. If polarization occurs only due to electronic displacements, as in elements such as germanium and silicon, there is no effect of the above type due to the motion of charge following the transition, and the optical and thermal activation energies are equal. This is consistent with there being no difference between the static and infra-red frequency dielectric constants. In ionic crystals these are however different due to the contribution of the ionic movement to the total polarization; this movement is too slow to contribute to the infra-red frequency dielectric constant, but because it is slow it leads in general to an appreciable difference between the two activation energies.

In the following sections it should therefore be recalled that the optical value may be different from the thermal equilibrium value when the semi-conductor is a compound. It will be realized that since the solid can be regarded as a large molecule, the same considerations apply when an electron is completely removed from it; the states before and after removal from a non-metal are again time-dependent and therefore the optical value for the depth of the conduction band below the external potential-energy level may be greater than χ.

6. *Photo-electric Emission.* The main threshold energy for photo-emission is $\chi + Q$, which corresponds with the ejection of electrons from the semi-conductor from the top of the valence band. At low temperatures such that impurity centres are occupied in n-type semi-conductors, there will be a small subsidiary emission at the lower frequency corresponding with $\chi + R$. If there is an appreciable electron density in the conduction band, there may be a small emission at the still lower energy χ. It should be noted that none of these energies corresponds with the thermionic work function $\chi + U$, though the difference may be very slight in a p-type semi-conductor, since the Fermi level may then be very near the edge of the valence band.

REFERENCES

HANNAY, N. B., *Semi-conductors.* Reinhold, 1959, p. 676.
HENISCH, H. K., *Rectifying Semi-conductor Contacts.* Oxford, 1957.
KINGSTON, R. H., *Semi-conductor Surface Physics.* Oxford, 1957.
WATKINS, T. B., *Progress in Semi-conductors V.* Heywood, 1960, p. 1.

CHAPTER 6

Optical Properties and Photoconductivity

1. *Optical Absorption.* If low energy radiation is incident on a semi-conductor of high purity at low temperature, there will be no absorption unless the energy gap is small because the conduction band is empty and the valence band is fully occupied. Absorption of energy would be expected when the energy of the radiation reaches the value $h\nu = Q$. We shall see below that the threshold is in fact at a slightly lower energy, because of the formation of 'excitons'. If impurity centres are present, and the temperature is low enough for them to be occupied, absorption is to be expected at the lower energy R. If however the conduction band is appreciably occupied, there will be an absorption of energy by the free electrons which can be excited to any of the higher energy states in the band. This absorption corresponds with that occurring due to the free electrons in a metal, and is proportional to λ^2 in the simplest case.

The process of raising an electron from an impurity atom to the conduction band corresponds with ionization of the centre, as indicated in Chapter 2. Compared with a hydrogen atom, ionization energy 13·6 eV, the ionization energy R in the solid is less by the factor $(m_e/m)(1/K^2)$, and is only about 0·01 eV for example for donors in germanium. However as with the hydrogen atom, stages of excitation can occur at lower energies in which the electron has energy levels above the ground state, but is still attached to the donor atom. These states can only exist and be resolved at low temperatures, but they can be detected and lead to a structure at low temperatures associated with the absorption peak at energy R. The first excited level of a donor centre is indicated at S above the ground state in Fig. 24.

Similarly the process of raising an electron from the valence band to the conduction band corresponds with removing it completely from the field of the positive hole which is formed by the transition. This involves the energy Q. Again there are excited states of lower energy, representing an electron remaining bound to the positive hole created by its ejection from the valence band. Such a pair, formed by an electron bound in the field of the positive hole, is called an 'exciton'. It has no charge, and can move in the crystal. Its lifetime is usually small, and may be terminated either by the absorption of further energy (e.g. thermal energy) which completes the separation of hole

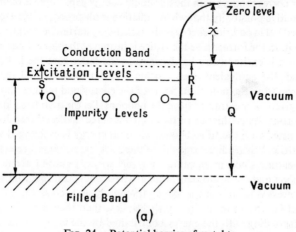

FIG. 24.—Potential barrier of metal to semi-conductor boundary

and electron, or by giving up the energy it possesses to another electron, or by recombination.

A further complication in this subject arises from the existence of selection rules for electronic transitions. When an electron is excited by absorption of a photon, energy and momentum must be conserved. The momentum of a photon is very small compared with that of an electron with thermal energy, so that if the whole of the photon energy is used in exciting an electron from a valence band to a conduction band, leaving a hole, the change in momentum of the electron must be negligible compared with its original momentum. This implies negligible change in wavelength, and a vertical transition in the energy level scheme shown dotted in Fig. 13. This is called a direct transition.

If the energy bands have the simplest form with the minimum of the conduction band and the maximum of the valence band both at $1/\lambda = 0$, the direct transition at $1/\lambda = 0$ will be the lowest energy transition possible and will lead to an absorption edge at a frequency corresponding with the energy gap Q.

If the bands are as in Fig. 14, however, no direct transition can occur corresponding with the minimum energy gap. There is then the alternative possibility that when radiation is absorbed, an electron is excited but in addition energy is given to the crystal lattice or extracted from it. In the former case the lattice is heated at the same time as the electron is excited (very locally) and in the latter case the lattice is cooled, the equivalent energy being added to that gained by the electron from the radiation. Some of the energy and momentum are now given to or extracted from the phonons, i.e. the quantized lattice vibrations. When this occurs the electrons make 'indirect' transitions contrasted with the 'direct' ones when no energy is exchanged with the lattice. With indirect transitions there may be a change in electron momentum since momentum is given to or removed from the phonons, and absorption can occur at a frequency corresponding with the lowest value of the energy gap (even in cases such as Fig. 14). It can in fact occur at an energy slightly less than this, the difference corresponding with the energy contributed by the crystal lattice.

The absorption coefficient usually increases when the energy of the radiation $h\nu$ reaches a value sufficient to cause direct transitions, compared with the value at lower frequencies when indirect transitions are occurring.

It may be noted that there is a further selection rule arising from the nature of the wave-functions corresponding with the successive energy bands. Thus as in the isolated atoms, transitions from a band derived from an s state are 'allowed' to a p-state band, but not to a d-state band. The latter are 'forbidden', but do take place with lower probability than the former.

Various laws arise relating the absorption coefficient and frequency near a band edge. Thus for direct allowed transitions, $\alpha^2 \propto h\nu - Q$, where Q is the minimum direct energy gap (Fig. 25a). For forbidden direct transitions, $\alpha \propto (h\nu - Q)^{3/2}$. With indirect transitions, it is found that the absorption edge has two branches, one with

$$\alpha^{1/2} \propto h\nu - Q + E_p$$

the other with $\alpha^{1/2} \propto h\nu - Q - E_p$. Q is now the minimum indirect energy gap, as in Fig. 14, and E_p is the energy associated with phonon emission or absorption, i.e. the energy extracted from or given to the crystal lattice.

The formation of excitons at frequencies less than Q/h (Fig. 24)

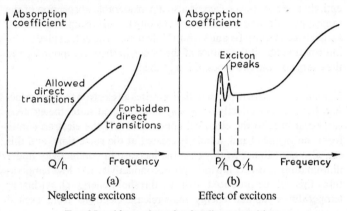

FIG. 25.—Absorption edge for direct transitions

when the transitions are direct, leads to a series of absorption lines, the principal one at a frequency corresponding with P, and others at higher frequencies corresponding with higher degrees of excitation, up to a 'series limit' at Q. One consequence of this is that the main absorption does not start from zero at the frequency Q/h as in Fig. 25(a), but from a plateau value as in Fig. 25(b), which is determined by the exciton behaviour. When the transitions are indirect however, exciton formation produces a tail on the absorption edge, down to a minimum energy $P - E_p$. Excitons combined with indirect transitions lead to absorption following the law $\alpha \propto (h\nu - P \pm E_p)^{1/2}$ for 'allowed' transitions and $\alpha \propto (h\nu - P \pm E_p)^{3/2}$ for 'forbidden' ones.

A further feature of the optical absorption spectrum remains to be described. In an ionic crystal there is a strong absorption of energy at a frequency, characteristic of the crystal lattice, at which the 'optical mode' of vibration is excited. This is a vibration forming standing waves in which neighbouring (unlike) ions are moving in opposite directions, unlike the longer wavelength 'acoustic' modes when neighbouring ions move in the same direction. The optical mode is excited by radiation at a frequency which is usually in the infra-red, e.g. at 61 μ for NaCl and 50 μ for InSb. The absorption is very strong in the alkali halide type of crystal, where the bonding is almost entirely ionic; however there is also a considerable absorption of the same type with compounds between Group II and Group VI elements, and between Group III and Group V elements. The details give useful information about the nature of the bonds in these compounds, and the charge on the two types of ion in them.

2. *Photoconductivity.* When radiation raises an electron to the conduction band, either directly or by way of an excited state, the electron can contribute to the electrical conductivity. If the electron comes from the valence band, a hole is created at the same time, and this can also contribute. In this case the increase in conductivity under illumination is called intrinsic photoconductivity. At low temperatures this will be produced with the threshold energy Q. At higher temperatures thermal energy may release electrons from excited states so that intrinsic photoconductivity may appear at the energy $h\nu = P$. At low temperatures the impurity levels are occupied in the dark, and illumination with energy R will lead to ejection of electrons into the conduction band in n-type material. This is extrinsic photoconductivity. Raising the temperature empties the donor levels and the response at energy R will disappear.

When incident radiation produces electron-hole pairs, the number of electrons in the conduction band exceeds the thermal equilibrium value by Δn_e, and correspondingly the number of holes in the valence band is increased by Δn_h. When the radiation is removed, these excess populations decay away as a result of recombination processes. The probability of a direct transition from the conduction band to the valence band, which would produce radiation of frequency $\geqslant Q/h$, is rather small and the lifetime of the excess carriers would be long if this were the only possible mechanism for recombination. In practice energy levels are usually present in the forbidden gap, due to impurities or lattice defects, such that a two-stage transition can occur. An electron may be captured into such a level, which may subsequenty trap a hole (or vice versa), the probability of each transition being much greater than that of the direct transition across the gap. The excess carrier lifetimes are greatly reduced by this mechanism compared with the 'perfect' crystal.

In the absence of radiation, the thermal equilibrium carrier densities represent a balance between the recombination processes and the thermal processes of generation of electrons and holes. When radiation is incident, the carrier densities increase and clearly the values of Δn_e and Δn_p for a given radiation will be greater the lower the recombination rates.

Any energy levels which are 'deep' in the forbidden energy gap, i.e. more than a few tenths of an electron volt below the conduction band or above the valence band, can act as recombination centres in this way. The details of the behaviour will depend on the position of the Fermi level, which determines to what extent the centres are occupied by electrons or holes. If they are deep enough, they have no direct effect on the free carrier densities in thermal equilibrium, since any increase they produce in recombination rate is balanced by a similar increase in rate of thermal generation. During the advancement of the technology of germanium, there was a period when the density of donor and acceptor (shallow) levels could be adequately controlled, giving good control of conductivity and Hall effect, but high densities of deep levels remained due to impurities and lattice defects, leading to high recombination rates and short lifetimes, less than a microsecond, when excess charge carriers were introduced by radiation or other processes. More recently however these imperfections have also been reduced in number, leading to lifetimes of the order of a millisecond, and to the possibility of detecting the radiation produced by the electron transitions direct from the conduction band to the valence band. There has so far been less success with silicon and with compound semi-conductors. As will be seen in Chapter 7, long lifetime of excess carriers is desirable in some types of p–n junction device as well as in photoconductors.

It should be emphasized at this point that the lifetime of excess carriers is determined by recombination with carriers of opposite sign, either directly or indirectly through traps. It has no connection with the relaxation time introduced in Chapter 1, § 4, which is determined by the rate at which an energy distribution returns to its thermal equilibrium state after perturbation, for example by the application of electric or magnetic fields. In this book we use the symbol τ for relaxation time and τ_l for lifetime.

Recombination rates at surfaces are frequently higher than would correspond to the bulk properties, due to adsorbed impurity atoms and charges in surface states. When the absorption coefficient is large, as may occur at frequencies exceeding Q, the radiant energy is all absorbed in the outer layers of the solid, so that the higher surface recombination rate may lead to relatively low photoconductivity. The photoconductivity may be considerably larger for radiation which is not so rapidly absorbed; then the electron or pair production occurs at greater depths in the material. There may therefore be a peak in photoconductivity near the absorption edge.

In order to detect intrinsic photoconductivity in a semiconductor such as germanium, the sample used must be of high purity, i.e. near intrinsic, so that the carrier density in the dark is not too high. The effect is then present at room temperature, with a threshold in Ge at 0·62 eV, and a quantum efficiency of unity for energies up to 2·5 eV, increasing at higher energy (Quantum efficiency of unity means one electron-hole pair produced per photon absorbed).

To detect extrinsic photoconductivity, due to electrons or holes liberated from impurity centres, the conditions depend on the activation energy involved. Thus for the usual donor impurities used to make germanium n-type, the activation energy is of the order 0·01 eV, corresponding to a wavelength of about 120 μ, in the far infra-red. With such small energy, the electrons are thermally activated out of the centres at temperatures above about 20° K, so that helium temperatures are necessary to detect the optical absorption and the photoconductivity due to these impurities. Doping with gold produces four levels in the forbidden gap of which one is at 0·2 eV below the conduction band and one 0·15 eV above the valence band. These lead to photoconductivity which is measurable at liquid air temperature.

Copper produces levels 0·04 and 0·32 eV above the valence band, and 0·26 eV below the conduction band.

The question of which levels are occupied in the dark when there are impurities with multiple levels depends on the degree of doping, on the temperature, and also on the presence of 'compensating' impurities, i.e. of donors in p-type material or of acceptors in n-type. These latter also serve to lower the dark conductivity, and so lower the background dark current above which the photoconductivity is to be detected.

Indium antimonide has become an important material for infra-red detection. Its variation of energy gap with temperature leads to a threshold for intrinsic photoconductivity at 7·5 μ at room temperature and 5·5 μ at liquid air temperature. It can now be made with low carrier density, and with reasonably good lifetime, though still less than the theoretical, which is ~ 1 μsec. However even with a rather poor lifetime useful sensitivity can be obtained at room temperature, though it is improved by cooling.

The extrinsic photoconductivity of InSb is interesting because the very low electron effective mass leads to an extremely small activation energy, about $7 \cdot 10^{-4}$ eV. Unfortunately the very low effective mass leads also to overlap of the orbitals for the impurity atoms even at low carrier densities. This causes a broadening of the energy level into a band, which overlaps the conduction band because their separation is so small. However a magnetic field of a few thousand oersteds produces a series of sharply defined energy levels, see § 4 below, one spaced $4 \cdot 10^{-4}$ eV below the bottom of the conduction band. By working at very low temperatures, below 2° K, the donor levels can be kept occupied in the dark, so that photoconductivity can be observed at $4 \cdot 10^{-4}$ eV, i.e. a wavelength of 3 mm.

In general the preparation of compounds between Group III and Group V elements is more difficult to control well than that of germanium and silicon, and that of Group II–Group VI compounds still more so. This is due to high melting points in some of them, and to a tendency to dissociate on heating with liberation of the more volatile constituent, so that departure from stoichiometry occurs readily. It is at first sight surprising therefore that some such compounds can be made in forms with high photoconductivity, since lifetimes much less than a microsecond would be expected. Nevertheless photo-conductivity occurs with a very high ratio of conductivity under illumination to that in the dark, and a large number of charge carriers per light quantum absorbed. This arises because of a mechanism not so far discussed.

In some of these materials it appears that impurity centres are present which have a double negative charge. These have a high probability of trapping a positive hole, but this type of capture does not lead to recombination, because the centre still has a negative charge and is unlikely to trap an electron. Thus there is a build-up of positive space charge throughout the crystal due to the holes in the traps, leading to an increase in the equilibrium population of free electrons in the conduction band. Thus Δn_e and therefore the photo-conductivity are much greater than the values which would be established by the recombination processes. The electrons move freely in the crystal and if one arrives at the positive electrode before recombining, another enters at the negative electrode; whereas the radiation can produce only one electron-hole pair initially per quantum absorbed, the effect just described can multiply the electron current by the factor τ_l/t, where τ_l is the lifetime of the electron and t the transit time of an electron across the crystal.

The factors which lead to the increased photo-conductive response have the disadvantage that they lead to a slow response time, in particular to a long decay time when the exciting light is cut off. The fact that the probability of trapping a hole was high in the centres under consideration means that the holes will be released slowly i.e. the apparent hole lifetime will be considerably longer than the 'true' lifetime as determined by recombination processes. While the holes remain present in the centres, the increase in electron population Δn_e remains greater than it would have been if determined by re-combination, i.e. the photoconductivity remains enhanced. This sluggish response is so far a considerable disadvantage; photocon-ductivity produced in this way is otherwise very useful in than the quantum efficiency may be as high as 10^4, and the ratio of light current to dark current may exceed 10^4 at an illumination of only 5 foot candles.

When CdS is in a fairly pure form, its resistivity is of the order

10^{12} ohm cm and there is a small photoconductivity with a peak at 5150 Å, near the absorption edge. Either halogen atoms or Group III atoms such as Ga or Al act as donor centres, with a level less than 0·05 eV below the conduction band, so that they produce an extrinsic conductivity which depends on their concentration. The presence of such centres raises the Fermi level and so alters the occupancy of the deep trapping levels. This permits some of these levels to act as hole traps in the manner described above, so raising the photoconductive response. The conductivity in the dark also increases however, and their ratio passes through a maximum at quite high resistivities, 10^8–10^9 ohm cm.

At the optimum doping, the photoconductivity is large, with a ratio of the order 10^4 as already indicated. It is possible to achieve this performance by doping with a donor alone, or by adding both donors and acceptors, in quantities which very nearly give compensation, with a slight donor excess. Copper and silver are used to provide acceptor centres in this way. In practice it is found easier to achieve a given resistivity by this procedure, using for example chlorine and copper, than by using the donor impurity alone.

When both the donor and the acceptor concentrations are quite high, e.g. near one part in thousand, the correct degree of compensation still leads to high photoconductivity, but now the peak in the spectral response is at wavelengths considerably longer than the absorption edge. Thus with copper the peak is at 7000 Å, and with silver near 6000 Å. This response arises from transitions from the acceptor levels to the conduction band, i.e. to extrinsic photoconductivity.

3. *Photoelectromagnetic Effect (P.E.M.)*. If intrinsic photoconductivity is produced near one face of a semi-conductor by light incident on it, an excess density of holes and electrons is produced near the surface. These diffuse away from the surface because of the concentration gradients. If a magnetic field is applied perpendicular to the plane of the diagram (Fig. 26), the holes and electrons separate and charge is transferred along the sample, so that one can observe either a short-circuit current or an open-circuit e.m.f. The theory shows that this effect depends on the square root of the lifetime τ_l, whereas the

straightforward photoconductivity depends linearly on τ_l. P.E.M. can be used both to measure short lifetimes and as means of radiation detection with short lifetime materials.

4. *Cyclotron Resonance.* If an electron is moving in an x–y plane when a magnetic field H is present in the z direction, then $m\,dv_x/dt = -\epsilon Hv_y$, $m\,dv_y/dt = \epsilon Hv_x$. These equations predict circular motion in the x–y plane with speed v in an orbit of radius $r, v = \epsilon rH/m$. The electron describes this orbit with the frequency $v_c = \epsilon H/2\pi m$, which is independent of the radius.

The angular momentum is $2\pi mr^2 v_c$ when the radius is r, and quantum theory requires this to be equal to $nh/2\pi$, where n may be any positive odd number.[1] With this proviso, $r^2 = nh/4\pi^2 mv_c$ and the

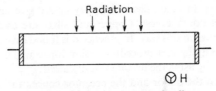

Radiation

$\bigodot H$

Fig. 26.—Photoelectromagnetic effect

kinetic energy of the electron is $\frac{1}{2}mr^2 4\pi^2 v_c^2 = 2\pi^2 mr^2 v_c^2 = nhv_c/2$. Thus the lowest energy which a free electron may have is $hv_c/2$, and the next higher state has energy $\frac{3}{2}hv_c$, and so on. In a solid the quasi-continuous conduction band of very closely spaced energy levels is therefore replaced for motion in the x–y plane by a sequence of levels spaced in energy by hv_c, with $v_c = \epsilon H/2\pi m_e$.

When radiation of energy hv_c is incident on the solid, transitions may take place between these equally spaced levels, causing absorption of energy from the radiation. With $H = 1000$ oe, $m =$ the mass of the free electron, v_c is near 3000 Mc/sec, thus there may be an absorption of energy at a microwave frequency. This is the 'cyclotron' frequency, and the absorption of energy can be detected at resonance, provided the electron is able to complete an orbit without being scattered by collisions in the lattice. The determination of the cyclotron resonance frequency in a known magnetic field will give a measure of the electron effective mass m_e, which in a solid is different from the free electron value. If the effective mass is anisotropic, its component values can be determined by varying the direction of the magnetic field in relation to the crystal lattice.

By raising the magnetic field, the resonance frequency can be raised until it reaches the infra-red region, particularly when the effective mass is small. This makes it possible to observe the resonance with less perfect material, since the time spent by the electron in an orbit is reduced. Shorter relaxation time τ can therefore be tolerated.

REFERENCES

General References

BUBE, R. H., *Photoconductivity of Solids*. Wiley, 1960.

BRECKENRIDGE, R. G., RUSSELL, B. R., & HAHN, E. E., *Proceedings Atlantic City Semi-conductor Photoconductivity Conference*. Wiley, 1956.

FAN, H. Y., *Infra-red Absorption in Semi-conductors. Repts. Progress Phys.* **19**, 107, 1956.

MCLEAN, T. P., The Absorption Edge in Semi-conductors, *Progress in Semi-conductors V*. Heywood, 1960, p. 63.

MOSS, T. S., *Optical Properties of Semi-conductors*. Butterworth, 1959.

(1) LANDAU, L., *Zeits. Phys.* **64**, 629, 1930.

CHAPTER 7

p–n Junction Devices

---

1. *p-n Junction Diodes*. If a p-type crystal is brought into contact with an n-type the presence of surface states prevents the establishment of a reproducible potential difference between them. If, however, in one crystal the impurity concentration and distribution can be controlled, such that one part of the crystal is p-type and the other n-type, then there is a p–n junction between the two regions, across which a potential difference exists, Fig. 27. The Fermi level is at the same height throughout, and in the p-type part of the crystal is near the top of the filled band. In the n-type part it is near the bottom of the conduction band, so that there is a potential difference between the n and p regions, slightly less than the height Q (in volts) of the forbidden zone. There is an equilibrium situation in which the flows of electrons and holes under the concentration gradients are balanced by the flows due to the potential difference across the junction. In the central region between the two dotted lines, the density of mobile charge carriers is very low compared with that in the p or n regions. The central region is therefore called the depletion layer, and it is across this layer that the potential difference is established.

If now the p type region is made more negative (reverse bias) it is more difficult for electrons to flow from n to p and more difficult for holes to flow from p to n. The electrons in an n type semi-conductor or the holes in a p type are called the 'majority carriers', and it is the flow of these into the opposite type of semi-conductor which is reduced. When they enter the region of opposite type they become minority carriers there, and they diffuse into the region of opposite type and move through it until they recombine with carriers of opposite sign. Let the current resulting from these two flows at zero bias be I_1.

In each region there is a small population of 'minority carriers' already present at zero bias in thermal equilibrium, i.e. holes in *n* type and vice versa. This population follows from the relation

$$n_e n_h = np = n_i^2$$

equation (3.6). The existence of these minority carriers permits small flows of holes from *n* to *p* and electrons from *p* to *n* across the junction and these flows are not affected by reverse bias. Let the sum of these

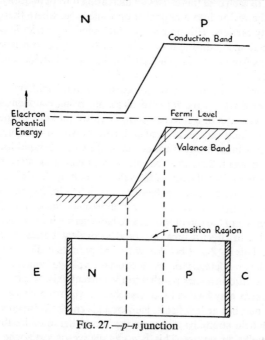

FIG. 27.—*p–n* junction

two currents be I_0. Then the total current through the junction at zero bias is $I_1 + I_0$. However this must be zero, so that I_1 is equal and opposite to I_0. Reverse bias does not alter the magnitude of I_0 but reduces I_1 by the factor $e^{-\epsilon V/kT}$ where V is the voltage applied. Thus a small net current flows following the law $I = I_0(1 - e^{-\epsilon V/kT})$ and saturating at the value I_0.

This reverse current increases with the rate at which hole-electron pairs are generated in the material. It therefore increases with increasing temperature, with decreasing energy gap, and with increasing density of recombination centres.

When, however, the p-type region is made more positive (forward bias) the barrier height is reduced and the flow of electrons from n-type to p-type and of holes from p to n is increased in the ratio $e^{\epsilon V/kT}$. In each case this causes an increasing flow of majority carriers from one region into a region of opposite type, where they become minority carriers. This process is called minority carrier injection by the junction. Again the flow of holes from n-type to p-type and of electrons from p to n is unaffected, so long as a barrier continues to exist. The net current is therefore $I_0(e^{\epsilon V/kT} - 1)$.

This relation can lead to currents of several milliamp at a few tenths of a volt in the forward direction, rising exponentially, and reverse currents of a microamp or so at several volts in the reverse direction, i.e. a very good rectification ratio. Above a limiting voltage however a breakdown effect occurs and there is a rapid increase in reverse current. This may be due to field emission, since provided the bias has raised the top of the valence band on the right above the bottom of the conduction band on the left, Fig. 27, an increasing field across the depletion layer will ultimately cause 'tunnelling' of electrons from the top of the valence band across into the conduction band, i.e. in effect a breaking of the covalent bonds between the atoms. This is 'Zener breakdown', and permits a diode to be used for voltage reference or as a constant voltage source, since the characteristic becomes parallel to the current axis. Alternatively the breakdown may be due to 'avalanching', when the charge carriers, few in number at low fields, gain enough energy between collisions at high field strengths to disrupt the bonds, i.e. to ionize the atoms, when collision occurs. This is a cumulative or avalanche process. Either type of breakdown is undesirable for the operation of a rectifier.

The complete theory of the diode shows that the value of I_0 is

$$I_0 = \epsilon \left(\frac{D_p p_n}{L_p} + \frac{D_n n_p}{L_n} \right) \text{amp/cm}^2 \qquad (6.1)$$

In this expression D_p and D_n are the diffusion coefficient for holes and electrons respectively, L_p and L_n are the respective diffusion lengths, while p_n is the density of holes in the n type material and n_p the density of electrons in the p type. The diffusion coefficient relates a rate of flow with a concentration gradient, e.g. via

$$D_p \frac{\partial^2 p}{\partial x^2} = \frac{\partial p}{\partial t}$$

and is related with the mobility of the particular carrier by the Einstein relation $D = kTu_0/\epsilon$. The diffusion length L indicates the depth to which carriers penetrate into a region in which they become minority carriers, i.e n into p or vice versa. This distance depends both on the diffusion constant and on the lifetime τ_l before recombination occurs with a carrier of opposite sign (usually via a trapping centre, see Chapter 6, § 2). The definition of L is usually in terms of the distance over which the density falls by the factor $1/e$, and the value is $\sqrt{D\tau}$.

It should be noted that the width of the depletion layer is not constant. It is a region of space charge; on the left between the dotted lines in Fig. 27 the positive (donor) impurity ions have too few free electrons to compensate their charge, while conversely on the right there are too few holes to compensate the charge on the negative (acceptor) impurity ions. The built-in field across the junction at zero bias has driven electrons away to the left and holes away to the right. When reverse bias is applied the increased field drives these free carriers still further apart, i.e. it increases the width of the depletion layer. This therefore lowers the capacity of the barrier. For the sharply-graded junction as shown, it is found that the capacity with reverse bias is proportional to $1/V^{1/2}$, where V is the total voltage across the junction; the capacity is also proportional to the square root of the impurity density.

2. *Tunnel Diodes.* In the tunnel diode both the n and the p type regions are heavily doped so that they are just degenerate, i.e. the Fermi level is a little above the bottom of the conduction band in the n-type region and below the top of the valence band in the p-type, as in Fig. 28. If now the width of the junction AB is small, ~ 100 Å, then the wave functions for electrons will penetrate appreciably across

the junction, i.e. electrons can tunnel across from n to p, and from p to n.[1] With zero applied voltage, the net flow across the junction must be zero. With 'reverse bias' in the sense used above, the p-type region is biassed negatively and the flow of electrons by tunnel effect from the valence band on the right to the conduction band on the left will increase rapidly. Similarly with forwards bias there is at first a rapid increase in the flow of electrons from the conduction band on the left to the vacant levels near the top of the valence band on the right, as shown at 0 in Fig. 29. However, the probability of transfer

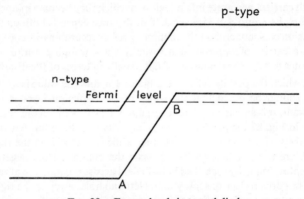

FIG. 28.—Energy levels in tunnel diode

across the gap is large only to a level at the same energy; lowering the top of the valence band on the right by positive bias, ultimately depresses it below the bottom of the conduction band on the left. There are then no empty levels in the valence band at the same height as the occupied levels in the conduction band. As this state is approached, the current begins to fall, and when this state is attained, the current should fall to zero. There is thus a maximum as shown on C in Fig. 29, followed by a region of negative slope from C to D. In practice the current remains greater than zero at D because of levels in the forbidden gap due to impurities, vacancies, etc. From D to E and beyond, the current rises again because of the injection process in the forward direction as described in section 1 above. The whole excursion from

0 to D is restricted to a range of two or three hundred millivolts depending on the material and the doping level.

Whereas in an ordinary *p–n* junction diode the speed of response depends on diffusion of carriers across the junction, the tunnelling process is extremely fast, with a time constant not greater than 10^{-12} sec, so that response time depends only on the circuit properties of the diode. The capacity of the diode per unit area of junction is high

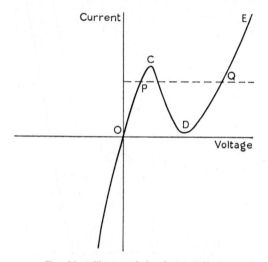

FIG. 29.—Characteristic of tunnel diode

because with heavy doping the depletion layer is very narrow (it is because it is narrow that tunnelling occurs), and because also capacity depends directly on impurity density. Thus junction area must be kept very small, but provided this is done the frequency limit and the speed of switching are both much higher than for ordinary junction diodes. Useful currents can be obtained in spite of the small area because the tunnel effect produces high current densities.

These diodes may be used either for switching at constant current from one stable state P to the other at Q, or for amplification using the negative characteristic CD.

3. *Solar Batteries*. When light is incident on a *p–n* junction, say on a thin *p*-type surface, the population of minority carriers, electrons in this case, is increased when the energy of the radiation exceeds the energy gap, as in the photoconductivity effect. The additional electrons may reach the junction before recombining, and if they do they

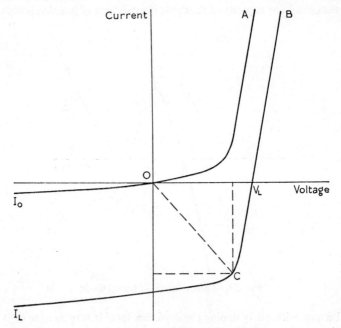

FIG. 30.—Characteristic for Photodiode

will flow across it constituting a current in the same direction as the reverse current which would flow when the junction is used as a diode. If the junction has a reverse voltage applied to it, the reverse current increases from the value I_0 to say I_L in the presence of the light, Fig. 30. The complete characteristic is moved from A to B, and then follows the relation $I = I_0(e^{\epsilon V/kT-1}) - I_L$. On open circuit, the voltage V_L will appear given by $e^{\epsilon V/kT} = I_L/I_0 + 1 \sim I_L/I_0$. The diode may therefore be used as a voltage source, and a load resistance may be placed across it, in which case the load line would be for example OC. The power output if the rectifier were perfect would be $V_L \times I_L$, and in practice may be as high as 80 per cent of this for optimum load resistance. The production of a voltage in this way is a photo-voltaic effect, and a photo-voltaic cell of this type used with the sun's radiation is described as a photo-voltaic solar converter or solar battery.

Since V_L varies inversely with I_0, it is desirable to keep I_0 as small as possible. The usual procedure is to dope the *p*-side rather heavily compared with the *n*, so that in equation (6.1), n_p is small compared with p_n. Then a low value of I_0 requires a small value of D_p/L_p, $= \sqrt{D_p/\tau_p}$, which calls for a low mobility and long lifetime. Further, the resistance of the *n* region must not be too high or its series resistance will lower the performance, and for a given *n*-type doping level, the value of p_n is determined by equation (3.6), and is proportional to $e^{-Q/kT}$, where Q is the energy gap of the semi-conductor. Thus V_L varies directly with Q. However the cell will respond only to photons with energy greater than Q, and the number of photons in solar radiation with energy greater than a given value E decreases as E increases. Thus I_L falls as Q rises. The result is that the power in the load which varies as $I_L V_L$ passes through a maximum as Q rises. The maximum occurs at $Q = 1\cdot5$ eV; this indicates that one could expect the best performance from CdTe or AlSb, which have this value of energy gap. These materials so far have short lifetimes, and the light is absorbed rapidly in them, so that the minority carriers generated by the light do not all reach the junction. For this reason silicon, with a lower absorption coefficient and a larger minority carrier lifetime in the best material, has the best performance so far although its energy gap is $1\cdot1$ eV, below the optimum. The best efficiency so far (1963) for the conversion of solar energy to electrical power is 14 per cent, for silicon *p–n* junction solar batteries.

4. *Junction Transistors.* By preparing a crystal with two junctions, either *p–n–p* or *n–p–n*, amplification can be obtained in the 'junction transistor'. In one version of this, the central portion is connected to ground by a base connection at *B* in Fig. 31; we will suppose that the

centre is a very narrow n-type region, and that p-type zones have a higher hole concentration p than the electron concentration n in the n-type zone. When the equilibrium is disturbed by applying a small 'forward' voltage across (1) and a larger 'reverse' voltage across (2), there are increased electron and hole currents across (1), the hole current being the larger, and decreased electron and hole currents across (2). However, provided the n-layer is thin enough, many of the holes flowing from left to right across (1) will diffuse through and

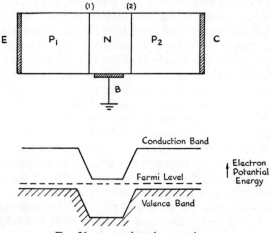

FIG. 31.—p–n–p junction transistor

reach (2) without recombining with electrons, in which case they will continue across (2) into the right-hand p-zone, and on to the contact C. Thus the forward voltage across (1), between E and ground, controls the flow of holes traversing the crystal to C. This control corresponds with the grid control of electrons in a triode valve; there is very little current flow to the base connection to the central zone.

From the discussion of the diode it will be recalled that the current across the emitter junction with forward bias is not entirely of holes from p to n; there is a small current of electrons in the opposite direction. The fraction of the total current which is carried by holes is called the injection efficiency of the junction for holes, and is inevitably less than 100 per cent. It is larger the greater the ratio of the doping level in the *p* region to that in the *n* region.

The current of holes passing from the base region to the collector junction *n/p* is reduced compared with the hole current injected by the emitter, because of recombination in the base region. The extent to which this occurs depends on the lifetime of the holes in the base region, and on the ratio of the diffusion length to the width of the base region. Thus one attempts to produce material with a high lifetime, and a large diffusion length, and to produce a device with as narrow a base region as possible.

Since the injection efficiency is less than 100 per cent, and since recombination occurs in the base region, the 'current gain' α is usually less than unity. This is defined as the change in collector current produced by a given small change in emitter current $-\partial I_c/\partial I_e$, when constant voltage V_{CB} is maintained between collector and base. The change in emitter current is produced by a small change in input voltage ΔV_i, while the collector current flows through a load resistance R_L, so that there is a change in output voltage across it equal to $\Delta I_C R_L = \alpha \Delta I_e R_L$. Although α is slightly less than unity, this voltage may be much larger than ΔV_i, indicating useful voltage and power amplification.

The simplest approximate expression for α under d.c. conditions is $\alpha = 1/[1 + \frac{1}{2}(W/L)^2]$ where W is the width of the base region and L is the diffusion length of holes in the base. Under a.c. conditions this becomes

$$\alpha = \frac{1}{1 + \frac{1}{2}(1 + i2\pi f \tau_p)(W/L)^2}$$

where f is the angular frequency and τ_p is the hole lifetime in the base. The 'cut-off' frequency is that at which α has fallen to 0·7 of its d.c. value, $(1/\sqrt{2})$, and with $W < L$ is given by $f_c = L^2/\pi W^2 \tau_p$.

The earlier types of *p–n* junction transistor were made by alloying for example dots of indium on either side of a thin wafer of *n*-type germanium. The smallest practicable base width W with this process is of the order $2 \cdot 10^{-3}$ cm, while the values of L and τ_p obtainable in practice are about 10^{-2} cm and 2 μsec respectively. These values lead to a maximum cut-off frequency near 10 Mc/s.

It should be noted that α is not in fact constant, but increases slightly as V_c becomes more negative as shown in Fig. 32. This is because the increasing value of V_c widens the space charge region at the collector junction, as discussed above in the diode case, and consequently

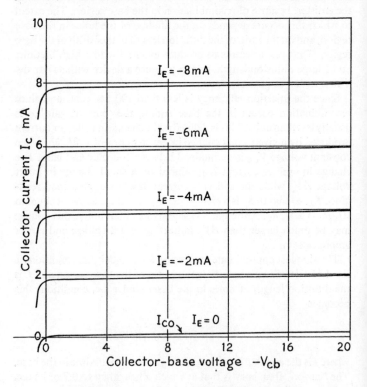

Fig. 32.—Grounded-base transistor characteristic.

reduces the base width W. This increases the hole concentration gradient in the base, and so raises the hole current, while at the same time since W is less the probability of recombination with electrons is decreased.

A more usual circuit arrangement than the above has the emitter,

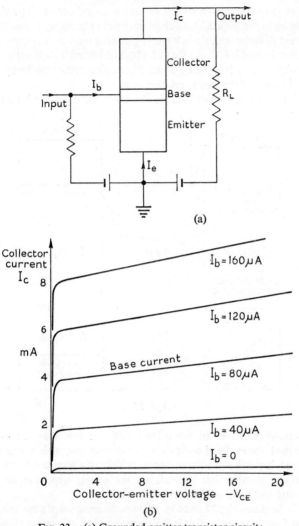

(a)

(b)

Fig. 33.—(a) Grounded-emitter transistor circuit;
(b) Grounded-emitter transistor characteristic.

rather than the base, common to the input and output. The circuit is shown in Fig. 33(a) and the characteristic in Fig. 33(b). The collector current I_C varies with the voltage V_{CE} as a function of the input (base) current I_B, and it is found that $\partial I_C / \partial I_B$ at constant V_{CE} has the value $\alpha_E = \alpha/1 - \alpha$. α_E is typically about 50, varying rather markedly with V_{CE} because of the small variation in α.

Common-collector circuits are also used, and of course in all cases

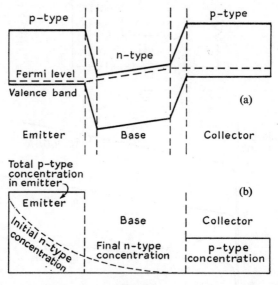

FIG. 34.

it is possible to use an n–p–n construction rather than the p–n–p described above. Semi-conductors other than germanium can also be used, in particular silicon. The suitability of a semi-conductor for transistor construction depends on the energy gap, and on the mobility and lifetime obtainable in practice.

The diagrams Fig. 32 and Fig. 33 show the presence of a current I_{CO} when I_E or I_R are zero. This is the current typical of a reverse biassed junction, and is given by equation 6.1. The minority carrier density, and therefore I_{CO}, rise exponentially with temperature at a rate depending on the energy gap, (equation 3.6). This increase limits the operating temperature to about $100°C$ for germanium transistors, and about $200°C$ for silicon.

The frequency limitation is due in part to the transit time of the minority carriers across the base region. For a given base width, this can be reduced by 'building-in' an electric field which will aid the holes to move across the base region. In a *p–n–p* transistor this can be done by establishing a concentration gradient of donors in the base, falling from the emitter junction to the collector junction. The energy level diagram is then as in Fig. 34 (a), with the potential energy for electrons rising on approaching the collector, so providing a field which accelerates holes. This effect may be achieved by first diffusing in a donor type impurity from the left, Fig. 34(b), and then alloying heavily doped emitter and collector regions .

5. *Controlled Rectifiers.* A *pn pn* structure can be used as a switch or as a controlled rectifier. If a positive voltage is applied to the *p* end, Fig. 35(a) and a negative one to the *n*, then there is a small forward bias applied to the junctions (1) and (3), giving predominantly an electron current through junction (1) and a hole current through junction (3). (n_1 and p_1 are doped more heavily than n_2 and p_2). The complete behaviour then depends on what happens at junction (2). So long as the current is small, junction (2) is in a stable state with a reverse bias across it, i.e. with the region n_2 positive with respect to p_2. This leads to a high overall impedence, most of the volt drop appearing across junction (2). If however the current is increased, a different stable state can be set up in which the potential gradient across junction (2) is reversed, i.e. it goes over to forward bias. This state has a very low overall impedance, so that the characteristic switches from A to B in Fig. 35(b). The switchover can be obtained either by increasing the overall voltage until the current is large enough to establish the unstable condition, or by applying a positive current to the region p_2 by a 'gate' contact, Fig. 35(c). As in a thyratron, the low impedance state once established is maintained when the gate current is removed, until the net current is allowed to fall below the value at A, following a reduction of the overall voltage.

The switchover from one stable state to the other occurs when $\alpha_1 + \alpha_2$ becomes equal to unity, where α_1 is the current gain of the transistor formed by $n_1 p_2 n_2$, and α_2 that of the transistor $p_1 n_2 p_2$. There is then a feed-back process between these transistors. An essen-

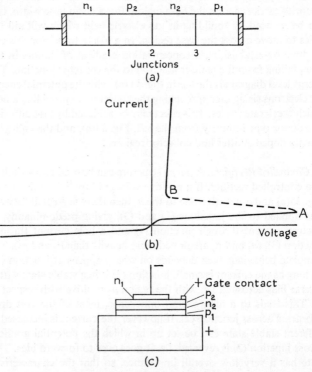

FIG. 35.—Controlled rectifier

tial condition is that α_1 or α_2 or both are appreciably below unity at low currents and rise with current to values such that $\alpha_1 + \alpha_2$ slightly exceeds unity. Note that although α is normally less than unity, values α exceeding unity are possible as a result of avalanche processes in the collector (junction 2) space charge region.

6. *Particle Counters.* If high energy particles are incident on a semi-conductor, each particle will release a large number of electrons and holes, in excess of the number present in thermal equilibrium. The energy used in creating a hole-electron pair is between 3 and 4 eV in silicon and germanium, and the number of pairs produced is very nearly proportional to the energy of the particles, thus a 10 MeV particle of any type will produce about $3 \cdot 10^6$ carrier pairs along its path through the semi-conductor. Such particles are rapidly brought to rest, the whole of their energy being released in path lengths well below 1 cm. The current pulse created by each particle can be amplified and fed to a counter, so providing a compact method for particle detection.

Successful operation requires a high resistivity material with a high mobility and low recombination trapping rate. It is necessary to collect the extra carriers at the electrodes as rapidly as possible to give a high counting rate and to minimize trapping. This requires high fields, and therefore high resitivity to minimize mean current and power dissipation. High mobility is therefore desirable combined with low carrier density. The recombination and trapping rates should be low, otherwise the pulse signal will be reduced, and moreover the proportionality between signal and energy may be lost. The type of trapping which introduces space charge will moreover alter the conductivity and the field and its distribution. While crystals of diamond, zinc sulphide, cadmium sulphide, gallium arsenide and intrinsic silicon are used as homogeneous crystal counters, it is easier at present to obtain the required properties in the neighbourhood of a reverse-biassed *p–n* junction. This type is widely used.

The same principles apply to the diffused junction type and to the surface barrier type. In both there is a very shallow *p–n* junction parallel to the surface of a crystal a few millimetres thick. The method of producing the junction differs in the two types. In the diffused junction, Fig. 36, a crystal of high quality lightly doped *p*-type silicon has a thin layer of *n*-type impurity diffused in from one surface, giving a high surface *n*-type concentration which however falls rapidly to give a junction at a depth of about 1μ. The high surface concentration permits a good peripheral contact to be made to the *n*-layer, which is biassed strongly positive. There is then a large reverse

8

bias across the junction, which produces a wide depletion layer, i.e. up to about half a millimetre, with a high field across it, of the order 10^4 volts/cm. The depletion layer has high resistivity, much higher than either the p or n layers, so that little current flows across it. (The reverse junction current discussed in Chapter 7, § 1 may be enhanced by carrier generation current in the depletion layer, but is nevertheless still very small). The electrodes are effectively at the boundaries of the depletion layer, and with such a high field and short distance, the collection efficiency is high and the collecting time is of the order 10^{-9} sec. The disadvantage is that the low width of the

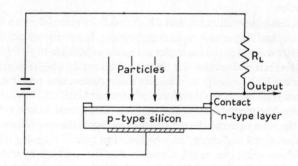

Fig. 36.—Particle counter

depletion layer limits the particle energy up to which the yield remains linear, to values near 10 MeV for protons and 40 MeV for α-particles. The n-type region must be very thin since it is not sensitive for counting, but does of course produce loss of energy of the particles. The conditions are similar to those in photocells as in Chapter 7, § 3 and counters must therefore be used in the dark.

The surface barrier type of counter utilizes the situation described in Chapter 5, § 1, Fig. 21. The surface of n-type germanium or silicon is allowed to oxidize, producing a shallow p-type inversion layer very near the surface, because of electrons accepted by the oxygen. A very thin metal contact must now be provided over the surface of the oxide, as its resistance is too high to permit a peripheral contact. This is done by evaporating a thin layer of gold over the surface. Except that the voltages must be reversed in sign, the conditions and the operation are as described for the diffused type.

7. *Light Emission from Junctions.* It has been indicated above that a forward biassed *p–n* junction 'injects' minority carriers across the junction into whichever region has the lower doping level, i.e. holes into an *n*-type region or electrons into a *p*-type region. These carriers diffuse across the region into which they are injected, and their number decays by recombination with carriers of opposite sign. Normally the recombination is via recombination centres, and leads to heating of the lattice, i.e. the energy is given to phonons, or if there is radiation, it is in the infra-red. If a crystal has a high degree of purity and perfection however, the recombination may be by transitions across the energy gap. When these are indirect transitions, there is still a considerable loss of energy to phonons, but the probability of emission of photons is higher for direct transitions, and where these occur useful light output may be obtained by injecting a high enough current density. The best example so far is GaAs, whose band structure permits direct transitions. The energy gap is 1.4 eV, so that the radiation is in the infra-red. It is expected that the addition of a limited amount of phosphorus will raise the gap sufficiently to give visible red radiation. (Too much phosphorus alters the band structure and leads to indirect transitions). The efficiency and brightness are low, but the efficiency can be raised by using a shape such as a hemisphere which reduces internal reflections.

At the time of writing (1963) a great deal of work is in progress to find suitable material with higher energy gap which will produce visible radiation. Work is in progress also to raise the brightness by obtaining 'laser' action, i.e. light production by stimulated emission. At very high current density (which therefore may require operation in pulses rather than d.c.) it is possible by injection across a junction to obtain a high density of electrons in levels at or near the bottom of the conduction band in *p*-type material, or conversely of holes in *n*-type material; in this situation stimulated emission may exceed stimulated absorption.[2] It is necessary to obtain a feed-back effect by internal reflection, so that the typical geometry is a diode with polished plane-parallel surfaces which are perpendicular to a flat *p–n* junction. The result of laser action is coherent nearly monochromatic radiation in a high intensity parallel beam.

It may be noted here that if a significant amount of radiative recombination occurs, a transistor can be developed in which there is a relatively large base width. This is the 'optotransistor', in which radiation produced near the emitter-base junction passes through the base and produces electron-hole pairs near the collector-base junction, allowing this junction to operate in the normal manner.

REFERENCES

General References

DEARNALEY, G., & NORTHROP, D. C., *Semi-conductor Counters for Nuclear Radiations.* Spon, 1963.

EVANS, J., *Fundamental Principles of Transistors.* Heywood, 1962.

GENTILE, S. P., *Tunnel Diodes.* Van Nostrand, 1962.

JONSCHER, A. K., *Principles of Semi-conductor Device Operation.* Bell, 1960.

MIDDLEBROOK, R. D., *An Introduction to Junction Transistor Theory*, Wiley, 1957.

MILLMAN, J., *Vacuum Tube and Semi-conductor Electronics.* McGraw Hill, 1958.

PHILLIPS, A. B., *Transistor Engineering.* McGraw-Hill, 1962.

SHOCKLEY, W., *Electrons and Holes in Semi-conductors.* Van Nostrand, 1950.

TAYLOR, J. M., *Semi-conductor Particle Detectors.* Butterworth, 1963.

TILLMAN, J. R., & ROBERTS, F. F., *An Introduction to the Theory and Practice of Transistors.* Pitman.

VALDES, L. B., *Physical Theory of Transistors.* McGraw Hill.

MORANT, M. J., *Introduction to Semiconductor Devices.* Harrap, 1964.

(1) ESAKI, L., *Phys. Rev.* **109**, 603, 1958.
ESAKI, L. & MIYAHARA, Y., *Solid State Electronics.* **1**, 13, 1960, *Brit. Journ. App. Phys.* **12**, 646-659, 1961.
(2) WANG, S., *Journ. App. Phys.* **34**, 3451, 1963.

CHAPTER 8

Secondary Emission

1. *General Considerations*. When electrons are incident on a solid, a proportion will suffer reflection. The proportion is larger for low-velocity electrons than for high-velocity ones, and the same as the proportion of internal electrons which are reflected when incident on the boundary (Chapter 1, § 9). The remaining electrons penetrate the solid, and lose energy to its electrons and to its lattice vibrations. Some will be totally absorbed after a number of collisions, and others will emerge in the direction of incidence with reduced energy. Some electrons may penetrate right through the solid, this possibility depending on its thickness and on the energy of the incident electrons. The interaction of the primary incident electrons with lattice electrons will raise the energy of some of the latter, and these will then lose energy in collisions, until either the extra energy is dissipated as heat, or by radiation if the electron can fall to a suitable lower level, or the electron reaches the surface with sufficient energy to escape. If it escapes from the surface upon which the primary beam is incident, it is called a true secondary, and can be collected at a positive electrode together with the reflected electrons and those which suffered inelastic collisions. The sum of the three is called the secondary emission of the solid, though the number of true secondaries is the important variable.

Some general features of the process can be deduced in a simple way. The higher the energy of the incident (primary) electrons, the farther will they penetrate and the greater will be the number of electrons in the solid which gain energy from the primaries. The penetration depth x is related with energy by the expression $E^2 = E_0^2 - Dx$ (Whiddington's law) where E_0 is the energy of the incident electrons and D is proportional to density of the material.

The maximum penetration depth is therefore $x_p = E_0^2/D$. The primary loses energy each time there is a collision process producing a secondary, so that the rate at which secondaries are produced is proportional to $-dE/dx$. This increases towards the end of the path of the primary. The secondary electrons have a maximum range of movement x_s, so that only those produced within a distance x_s from the surface can escape. On this basis we can consider the effect of increasing the incident energy of the primaries. So long as x_p is less than x_s, an increase of E_0 will cause an increase in the number of true secondaries emitted. When however x_p becomes greater than x_s, further increase in E_0 and therefore in x_p will cause a reduction in this number; the total number of secondaries created will continue to increase with E_0, but the number which can reach the surface will decrease, as the productive region near the end of the path of the primaries is at a depth greater than x_s. The rate of production near the surface decreases as E_0 rises, since the energy of the primaries near the surface remains nearly equal to E_0. Thus the number of secondaries emitted goes through a maximum and decreases as primary energy continues to rise. At constant primary energy the secondary current is proportional to the primary current, and the ratio is the secondary emission coefficient δ of the solid, which has therefore a maximum value δ_m which occurs at a primary energy E_m. It is found that the secondary range x_s is not dependent on the density of the solid. Since D does depend on density, δ_m is higher the denser the material, since x_p is less for a given E_0, the higher the density. For the same reason, δ at a given energy is higher for oblique than for normal incidence.

For metals the values of δ_m range from about 0·6 to 1·7, as shown in Table 2. E_m varies between 100 and 800 volts. There is a uniformity of behaviour in that if δ/δ_m is plotted against E_0/E_m, all metals give the same curve. The values of δ_m are not high because the secondaries lose energy by colliding with the electron population already in the metal. The value of x_s is only about 30 Å.

The average energy loss by a primary when creating a secondary is approximately 30 eV. The secondaries reach the surface with average energy approximately 10 eV, and after escape, there is a further reduction by the work function ϕ, so that the mean energy is 3–5 eV. This is high compared with the energy of electrons emitted by therm-

TABLE 2

Element	δ_{max}	E_0 at max. δ, volts
Aluminium	1·0	300
Antimony	1·3	600
Barium	0·8	400
Beryllium	0·6	200
Bismuth	1·5	800
Cadmium	1·1	400
Caesium	0·7	400
Carbon	1·0	300
Cobalt	1·2	500
Copper	1·35	500
Gold	1·5	700
Iron	1·3	400
Lead	1·1	500
Lithium	0·55	100
Magnesium	0·95	300
Mercury	1·3	600
Molybdenum	1·2	400
Nickel	1·3	500
Niobium	1·2	400
Platinum	1·6	700
Potassium	0·7	300
Rhenium	1·3	800
Rubidium	0·8	400
Silver	1·5	800
Tantalum	1·35	600
Thallium	1·7	650
Thorium	1·1	800
Tin	1·35	500
Titanium	0·9	300
Tungsten	1·4	700
Zirconium	1·1	300

ionic emission and in consequence there is by comparison only a small increase in δ when ϕ is lowered for a metal for example by deposition of a monatomic film. For the same reason, the value of δ is not sensitive to temperature.

It may be noted that comparing different metals, there is a trend for high values of δ_m to be associated with high values of ϕ, since the latter are associated with high density. Thus in such a comparison the effect of ϕ on secondary emission is opposite to that on primary emission.

2. *Secondary Emission from Insulators and Semi-conductors.* Provided that its energy exceeds Q eV, the primary electron can interact with an electron in the valence band, producing an electron-hole pair. If its energy is large enough, it may of course interact with an inner-shell electron. The secondary electron in the conduction band can now lose energy by interaction with lattice vibrations, or if its energy exceeds Q, by creating further electron-hole pairs. In an insulator or low-conductivity semi-conductor it will not lose energy as in a metal by interaction with free electrons in the conduction band.

If the secondary electron reaches the boundary with kinetic energy greater than χ it may escape as a true secondary (Fig. 24). The probability of this is high if χ is less than Q, since secondaries with energy less than Q can lose energy only to the lattice vibrations. Thus in insulators with $\chi < Q$, the secondary emission may be much larger than in a metal. The much smaller rate of loss of energy of the secondary indicates also that x_s will be larger in such an insulator or semiconductor than in a metal, so that the primary energy at which δ is a maximum will be larger. Examples of high values of δ_m and E_m are shown in Table 3.

In an insulator or semi-conductor with $\chi > Q$, the secondaries will interact with the electrons in the valence band in much the same way as with the free electrons in a metal, losing energy equally rapidly so that the values of x_s and of δ_m and E_m are similar to those for metals. This is the case for boron, silicon and germanium as in Table 3. If with $\chi < Q$, the material is heavily doped or has a high intrinsic conductivity, δ_m will be less than in the low conductivity state because of interaction with electrons in the conduction band. Thus δ can vary with doping level and with temperature in a good secondary emitting material.

We have neglected so far the problem of the current flow which must occur in an insulator if it is to continue giving secondary emission. The primary electrons enter the insulator, produce second-

aries, and unless the field is very large or the insulator is a thin film
on a metal base, a space charge is formed in the crystal. If the initial
secondary emission coefficient is greater than unity, at the primary
voltage E_0 employed, the outer layers of the insulator will show a net
loss of electrons, and the resultant positive space charge will attract
back some of the emitted electrons; in equilibrium the surface of the

TABLE 3

Material	δ_{max}	E_0 at max. δ, volts
Boron	1·2	150
Germanium	1·2	400
Silicon	1·1	250
Selenium	1·3	400
$Ag_2O + Au$ or Ni	1·2	600
$MoO_2 + Pt$	1·2	
MoS_2	1·1	
Cu_2O	1·2	400
Al_2O_3	2·8	400–1200
BeO	5–10	400–800
BaO	5	600
CaO	5	600
$Cs_2O + Ag$	6	500
Cs_3Sb	6	700
KCl	7	1200
Mica	2·4	400
NaCl	7–10	700
ZnS	1·8	350

insulator will take up a positive potential with respect to E_0, which
will increase until the effective secondary emission coefficient becomes
unity, i.e. the surface will charge up to the potential B (Fig. 37).
Similarly if the primary voltage E_0 is greater than B, a negative surface
space charge will be created, which will develop until the surface
potential has fallen to the value B. If E_0 is less than A, a negative
charge develops which reduces the surface potential to zero. This will
also happen for all values of E_0 if the maximum value of δ is less than
unity. Thus with normal voltage gradients in the solid and with all

except very thin specimens, the insulator surface takes up a potential of either zero or B, (the second crossover point) and no measurement of δ can be made.

The situation is different if the thickness of the insulator is small, not much greater than the secondary range x_s. If δ is greater than 1, the positive potential at the surface of the insulator will then create a volt drop across it which may be sufficient to maintain a secondary current of electrons, drawn from the underlying metal.

Under these conditions it is possible to obtain the true secondary emission current typical of the insulator, with a surface potential only

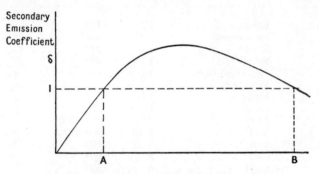

FIG. 37.—Primary electron potential, E_0 in volts.

slightly greater than E_0. The requirements are rather critical in that if the thickness is less than x_s, the maximum value of δ which the material will give will not be obtained, while if it is much greater, charging up will occur. The surface potential corresponding with the observed value of δ is then not known. Some experimental values for insulators shown in Table 3 were obtained with thin films.

3. *Malter Effect.* Under the conditions where $\delta > 1$, the positive potential developed at the surface of the semi-conductor may lead to a volt drop across it as described in the previous section. Although frequently small, this may represent a considerable potential gradient through the film and at the surface of the underlying metal. In extreme

cases this may exceed 10^6 volt/cm, in which case field emission may be drawn from the metal, and breakdown may occur across the insulator. This effect was first observed by Malter (1) for caesium oxide on aluminium oxide on aluminium, but has since been observed for other insulators. It can lead to an apparent value of δ of some hundreds or thousands. Since these large values are due to the charging up of the outer layers, time-delay effects are observed both in the establishment of them after applying the primary beam, and in their decay after removing it. The decay may in fact occupy many minutes or even some hours, during which time scintillations are observed in localized regions where breakdown takes place. Potential differences in the range 1–100 volts are established across films of thickness from 10^{-6} to 10^{-5} cm.

4. *Bombardment Induced Conductivity.* If an insulator or poor semi-conductor is bombarded with electrons and if a field is applied across it, then under some conditions the secondary electrons produced in the solid can be collected by the field electrodes. This is easiest to achieve under pulsed bombardment conditions in a high resistivity long-lifetime crystal, and the situation is then very similar to the homogeneous particle counter described in Chapter 7, § 6. Diamond and cadmium sulphide show current multiplication of this type, but the subject has not been very much studied. Multiplication has been observed under d.c. conditions in thin films of selenium.

One reason for interest in this topic is the possibility of accelerating the secondary electrons within a phosphor layer in an attempt to produce electroluminescence to enhance the luminescence of a phosphor layer under electron bombardment. Zinc sulphide is the material of importance in this context.

5. *Decay of Secondary Emission.* In secondary emission multipliers thin films of magnesium oxide, beryllium oxide, caesium oxide or caesium antimonide are used to provide high secondary emission coefficients. One difficulty with thin high resistance films is the tendency for the coefficient to decay with time, which is present to a varying degree with all types of films. The effect is more severe the higher the current density. This is an important factor in limiting the

usefulness of secondary emission multiplication to photo emitters rather than to thermionic devices, where useful current densities would be much higher.

The alkali halides are examples of materials showing a marked decay effect, thus the initial values of δ_m are large, as in Table 3, but during continued electron bombardment of the surface, δ_m falls in a few hours by factors of 5–10. At time the same the halide develops colour due to the formation of 'colour centres' (F-centres). These are formed when either incident primaries or secondaries liberated in the crystal are trapped at vacant negative-ion lattice points. This coloration under electron bombardment was used to display an opaque trace on an oscillograph screen, in contrast with the ordinary cathode-ray-tube screen which displays a luminescent trace. The colour centres have an absorption band when illuminated, corresponding with an energy of about 2 eV, i.e. the wavelength is about 600 mμ, and if the electron bombardment ceases, illumination with light of this wavelength ejects the electrons from the colour centres and restores them gradually to the negative ions from which they came.

At the same time as the occupation of negative ion vacancies, there may be an irreversible process if the energy of the bombarding electrons is sufficient to form electron-hole pairs, i.e. if it exceeds about 1·5 times the forbidden gap. The production of a hole implies the removal of an electron from a negative ion and therefore the formation of a halogen atom which is then only loosely bound to the crystal lattice, since the electrostatic Coulomb force has been destroyed. If ions and atoms are mobile in the crystal as well as electrons and holes, this process can lead to the loss of halogen atoms from the crystal, while alkali metal ions can retain electrons and coagulate to form colloidal specks of metal in the crystal. Thus there is a decomposition process which will lead ultimately to the destruction of the film. This decomposition corresponds with the photochemical processes which occur in many types of material, and in particular in the photographic process in the silver halides.

The small particles of alkali metal will have a work function higher than the electron affinity of the alkali halide, and will therefore tend to collect electrons so reducing the range of the secondaries in the crystal. The particles themselves have a very low secondary emission coefficient, so that the decomposition process will cause a marked drop in δ_m. Whether there is any contribution to the decay from the formation of F-centres as distinct from the decomposition process is not firmly established.

In the divalent oxides a similar situation exists, with some evidence that magnesium and beryllium oxides are more stable than barium or strontium oxide. The latter decompose on bombardment with complete liberation of oxygen, leaving a film of barium or strontium metal with low secondary emission. Such a film is readily evaporated from the underlying metal on heating. If the film is heated after partial decomposition, the secondary emission coefficient is restored to its initial value, presumably because of dispersal or evaporation of the grains of metal. The greater stability of magnesium and beryllium oxide is presumably due to their refractory nature, which indicates higher bond strengths and lower mobility of ions and atoms.

It may be noted that the presence of a limited number of donor centres as distinct from coagulated metal particles does not lower δ_m in these oxides. The donor centres are either isolated impurity atoms or isolated centres resembling F-centres, with densities normally less than $10^{18}/cm^3$. Such centres 'activate' BaO and SrO as thermionic cathodes, and by raising the electrical conductivity, permit these oxides to be used as secondary emitters in quite thick layers, e.g. 0.1 mm. In the absence of donor centres such oxide layers would show severe charging-up effects but after activation this is avoided provided the temperature is raised to 200–$300°$ C. The values of δ_m for such activated layers are included in Table 3, and are not significantly different from other similar oxides.

Caesium oxide and caesium antimonide are semi-conductors discussed further in Chapter 9. They are sufficiently stable at current densities below 1 ma/cm^2 for extensive use in photo-electric secondary emission multipliers.

An important practical consequence of the decomposition is that if compounds are present on the surfaces of electrodes in electronic tubes, they may liberate gas under electron bombardment, which may travel to the cathode and raise its work function following adsorption. This 'poisons' the cathode emission and is an important effect in both thermionic and photo-electric tubes.

REFERENCES

General References

BRUINING, H., *Physics and Application of Secondary Electron Emission*. Pergamon, 1954.

HACHENBERG, O., & BRAUER, W., Secondary Emission from Solids, *Advances in Electronics and Electron Physics XI*. Academic Press, 1959, p. 413.

(1) MALTER, L., *Phys. Rev.* **50**, 48, 1936.

CHAPTER 9

Thermionic Cathode Coatings

Barium–Strontium Oxide

1. *General Features.* The 'oxide cathode' usually consists of barium/ strontium oxide, though sometimes calcium oxide is added. It is in the form of a coating about 0·1 mm thick, applied to the surface of either nickel or platinum. The emission must lead to the passage of electrons from the metal to the oxide, and through the oxide, so that the metal to semi-conductor contact and the semi-conductor itself are both involved.

This type of cathode remains important in thermionic devices since it is the most economical in power, as it operates at 700°–800° C with a power requirement of only 2–3 watts/cm². The emission is limited under d.c. conditions to a few hundred ma/cm², but much higher values are obtainable under pulsed conditions. The electrical resistance of the coating is a major disadvantage for high current density operation, and the newer types of cathode[1] provide a reservoir of a barium compound in or beneath a porous nickel or tungsten matrix. Barium is produced and migrates to the metal surface, where it is adsorbed, leading to a work function of about 1·6, and to useful emission at temperatures between 900 and 1100° C.

Reverting to the oxide cathode, it was found early that a mixture of BaO and SrO gave better performance than pure BaO, although this was greatly superior to SrO. It now appears that the addition of CaO in small quantity to a mixture of nearly equal amounts of BaO and SrO gives further improvement. The coating most thoroughly studied is, however, one with equimolecular proportions of BaO and SrO, and our discussion will be confined to this case. The coating is formed by the application of a mixture of carbonates to the metal base which are decomposed to oxides in vacuum at 900–1150° C.

The coating density is usually of the order unity, representing considerable porosity, since the bulk density of the carbonates is 4·5. The particle size of the carbonates is usually 1–12 μ, which is preserved in the oxide. The final state of the oxides is a solid solution, which, however, is homogeneous for only a very short time, as the outer layers are found early in operation to consist of pure SrO. Crystal growth occurs above 950°C, and there is therefore some growth during the processing treatments at 900–1100°C, but it is probably insufficient to convert single particles to single crystals.

The discussion will be confined to the case where good conditions are maintained, i.e. we shall not consider 'poisoning' due for example, to exposure of the carbonates to sulphur, or of the oxides, after decomposition, to water vapour. If the base metal is very pure nickel or platinum, shortly after a vacuum heat treatment designed to give complete conversion to oxides and fairly complete solid solution, the emission is usually small (say 5 mA/cm^2 at 800°C), and does not improve during further heat treatment without drawing emission, unless the pressure is very low, well below 10^{-6} mm. The initial emission is larger (say 100 mA/cm^2 at 800°C) with nickel containing a trace (0·1–0·3 per cent) of Mg or Al, and intermediate with similar traces of Si or Ti. In all cases, the emission increases while current is drawn, with the coating at 850–950°C, and becomes finally, under good vacuum conditions, about 1 amp/cm^2 at 800°C in d.c. tests. The time to reach this state is longer with the pure Ni or Pt, but the final state is the same. If a Richardson plot is made of log I/T^2 against $1/T$, this state is characterized in d.c. measurements by a work function near 1 eV, and an A value from 10^{-2} to 10^{-1}. 'Saturated emission' is frequently difficult to define, since there is a slow departure from space-charge conditions, and Schottky's law is not obeyed, but these figures refer to the estimated maximum current at which the 3/2 power law still applies.

It is found that the instantaneous current, available immediately on applying a collector voltage, is greater at the higher temperatures than the steady state (d.c.) current. This may be studied either by discharging a condenser through a diode or working with repetitive pulses, each a few microseconds long, and separated by a time sufficient for recovery from any decay effect, i.e. greater than about

$\frac{1}{1000}$ sec. The emission under these 'pulsed' conditions may be about 10 amp/cm^2 at 750°C, and is represented by a work function near 1·5 eV, and an A value near 100.

With continued operation, the mean Ba concentration decreases, and when this occurs, both pulsed and d.c. emission fall, until when the coating is wholly SrO, the emission is about $\frac{1}{1000}$ of the initial. The rate of loss of Ba is very temperature dependent, and complete loss by evaporation requires many thousands of hours below 800°C, and about 3000 hours at a true temperature of 900°C. The rate of loss is not dependent on current density in d.c. operation below 0·5 amp/cm^2, though at higher current densities it should become possible for electrolytic loss to exceed evaporation loss. There may be a deceptive decrease in d.c. emission in operation, which is not accompanied by appreciable loss of Ba, nor by decrease in pulsed emission. This is due to an increase in the decay effects, discussed below.

The increase in emission in the early stages of operation is accompanied by an improvement in vacuum, and an increase in coating conductivity. It is described as activation. It is believed to be due to the formation of donor centres, which are distributed through the coating and may be adsorbed on its surface. These centres could *a priori* be oxygen ion vacancies, or singly charged Ba$^+$ or Sr$^+$ ions. Certainly barium is volatilized from the coating, together with BaO, and chemical tests have shown atoms with a high affinity for oxygen and water vapour to be present after activation at a concentration of the order 10^{18} atoms/cm^3. In the presence of traces of Mg or Al, the donor formation is assisted by reduction, but with pure Ni or Pt the process of electrolysis is necessary, unless the vacuum is extremely good. The proportion of the total current carried by ions in the earlier stages of operation at 900°C is about $2·10^{-4}$, falling quickly to about $1·10^{-5}$. It is clear from the life encountered in practice, and the independence of life and current density below 0·5 amp/cm^2, that this proportion at 800°C falls rapidly to a figure below 10^{-6}. Electrolysis, therefore, may play an important part at first, but only a very minor one during the main part of the life of the cathode.

During the reduction process a layer is formed between the core metal and the coating, consisting of a compound of BaO with the oxide of the metal additive, thus nickel containing silicon forms a layer

9

of barium orthosilicate. Between 700° and 800° C this has much higher resistivity than the BaO/SrO and forms a barrier layer with a rectifying action, causing high resistance for electrons flowing from metal to coating, which is the direction for emission. In general with an oxide coating in a diode we shall expect deviations from the space-charge law, because the measured voltage is applied between core and anode, and the voltage across the space-charge zone is less than this because of the voltage drop across the coating. This will always be the case, but in the presence of a high-resistance interface the effect may be large, and the space-charge characteristic may be replaced by a characteristic resembling a rectifier in the high-resistance direction, i.e., there is a 'knee' which represents saturation of emission through the interface barrier layer, and not saturated emission from the outer surface. This effect may be detected at the lower temperatures, e.g. 600° C with the orthosilicate layer, and is sometimes present when Mg is the additive; here the layer is of MgO, there being no reaction between MgO and BaO. The other compounds formed in this way, e.g., Ba aluminate and orthotitanate, have lower resistivity than the orthosilicate, and give intermediate behaviour The thickness of these layers is of the order 10^{-4} cm when there is about 0·1 per cent of the impurity, but grows to about 10^{-3} cm. when there is 0·5 per cent or more of the impurity. The high resistance of these layers is most marked after periods of stand-by with the cathode hot but no anode current. These layers may, in addition, increase the thermal emissivity of the core surface, which is important, since this surface can 'see through' the coating. With the pure nickel, no interface is formed, and the rectifying action of this contact is unimportant in practice. In the presence of oxygen however, nickel reacts with BaO at 700°– 800° C to form compounds with low emission. It may be noted that the capacity and resistance of the interface are always such as to lead to a very small associated time constant, so that the interface resistance, if important, can be detected in operation with microsecond pulses as well as with longer duty cycles.

In continuous operation, it is not possible to draw high current densities from oxide cathodes, because apart from the decay effects, the resistance of the coating sets a limit due to $I^2 R$ heating. The resistance of a typical coating may be of the order 3–5 ohms per cm^2 at

750–800°C and, unless there is appreciable conduction cooling, the current cannot therefore exceed about 1 amp/cm^2, since the coating radiates only about 3 watts/cm^2 at 800°C. Moreover the current flow is not uniform, and high local current density causes excessive local heating and loss of coating by decomposition and evaporation, and damage by fusion. In pulsed operation with low-duty cycle, the mean heating may be very small although the current density may be some tens of amp/cm^2. It is possible, therefore, to explore the current beyond saturation even at high temperature. It is found that Schottky's law for metal is not obeyed, and the current increases beyond the knee very considerably. It is frequently found that $\log I$ is proportional to $\log V$, indicating a law of the type $I = \alpha V^{\beta}$, where β increases with temperature, and is larger for a rough surface than one which is sprayed wet and relatively smooth. The highest current density which can be drawn in pulsed operation is about 70 amp/cm^2, beyond which discharges occur between anode and cathode, leading to arcing and disruption of the coating. These discharges occur at lower currents if interfaces are present, due either to the I^2R heating in the interface layer or to dielectric breakdown across it.

2. *Conductivity.* After formation of the oxide by heating during pumping, a cathode coating has a conductivity of the order 10^{-4} ohm^{-1} cm^{-1} at 1000°K. $\log \sigma$ plotted against $1/T$ gives a linear relation, with a slope between 1·0 and 1·5 eV. When the coating is activated, either by heating on Ni containing Mg or Al or by drawing emission in other cases, the conductivity rises and the slope falls, thus the curves vary with time of activation, forming part of the family of curves in Fig. 15. The increase in σ is associated with the improvement in vacuum which always accompanies activation, and subsequent deterioration of vacuum can readily restore the state with slope near 1 eV. There is a tendency to develop a second typical state with σ about 10^{-3} at 1000°K, and slope near 0·7 eV. A lower slope, near 0·3 eV, is then sometimes detected at lower temperatures, e.g. below 700°K. This is the state after activating for some hours, when the thermionic behaviour is as referred to in the previous section. States have been described with σ as high as 10^{-2} at 1000°K, in which case the slope at high temperatures has fallen to about 0·3 eV but this

behaviour is not readily obtained, is not reproducible and marked temperature hysteresis effects are present.

The (1949) Loosjes–Vink theory[2] associates part of the conductivity with the porosity of the coating. It attributes conductivity to a current flow through crystals and their contacts, in parallel with a flow through the space charge in the interstices of the coating, between the particles. This model requires $R/2$ for well-activated coatings to have the low-temperature value of the slope of $\log \sigma$ against $1/T$, i.e., about 0·3 eV. The slope in the central temperature zone, near 1000° K, would then be the resultant of this low slope for conductivity through the crystals, combined with a slope similar to the work function for pore conductivity. There is support for this theory from later work on the thermo-electric properties of these coatings.

It appears that a compact coating is sometimes encountered with a high particle conductivity such that the pore contribution is not significant below 1100° K; the slope may then be below 0·5 eV up to this temperature. More typically however the two contributions are present in parallel between 7000 and 1100° K, the pore contribution becoming negligible below about 700° K. At lower temperatures it is sometimes possible to detect a contribution with a still lower temperature variation. This seems likely to be due to surface conductivity arising from a higher concentration of electrons or holes than in the interior of the crystals.

3. *Surface Conditions.* The nature of the donor centres is not definitely established, nor is the situation at the surface of the grains. It is clearly possible for the outermost surface layer to consist wholly of oxygen, or wholly of barium/strontium, though more probably it has some intermediate composition. In the first case the excess of oxygen compared with the lattice composition would provide electron acceptors at the surface, so establishing a positive space charge below it, and raising the work function as in Fig. 20 or 21. The situation is then as in Fig. 38(a). Conversely in the second case, (b), holes are trapped at the surface at the excess Ba/Sr, and the negative space charge below the surface lowers the work function. It is unlikely that these extreme cases are attained in practice, but small changes in either direction about the mean state (c) will produce considerable changes in the

work function. This will therefore be very dependent on the nature and pressure of the residual gas, and on the temperature. The presence of oxygen or oxidizing gas will tend to produce the high work-function state (a), and will also reduce the density of donors whatever their nature. This will raise the resistivity of the crystals and the overall effective resistivity of the coating.

During continuous operation drawing current the emission often decays because of (1) ionization of residual gas, leading to bombardment of the coating by positive ions. (2) liberation of gas from electrodes under electron bombardment; this may include electronegative gas formed by decomposition of thin films on the electrodes, e.g. of

$$
\begin{array}{ccc}
\begin{array}{l}
O^{--}\ Ba^{++}\ O^{--} \\
Ba^{++}\ O^{--} \\
O^{--}\ Ba^{++}\ O^{--} \\
Ba^{++}\ O^{--} \\
O^{--}\ Ba^{++}\ O^{--} \\
Ba^{++}\ O^{--}
\end{array}
&
\begin{array}{l}
O^{--}\ Ba^{++} \\
Ba^{++}\ O^{--}\ Ba^{++} \\
O^{--}\ Ba^{++} \\
Ba^{++}\ O^{--}\ Ba^{++} \\
O^{--}\ Ba^{++} \\
Ba^{++}\ O^{--}\ Ba^{++}
\end{array}
&
\begin{array}{l}
O^{--}\ Ba^{++} \\
Ba^{++}\ O^{--} \\
O^{--}\ Ba^{++} \\
Ba^{++}\ O^{--} \\
O^{--}\ Ba^{--} \\
Ba^{++}\ O^{--}
\end{array} \\
(a) & (b) & (c)
\end{array}
$$

FIG. 38.—Surface of barium oxide.

BaO or $BaCl_2$ which originated in the coating itself (coatings may contain traces of chloride, or it may be formed by reaction with chlorine liberated from the glass envelope) (3) an ionic movement in the coating under the potential gradient across it, drawing positive ions into the coating and negative ions out to its surface. This will raise the work function, as the surface changes in the direction (b) to (a) in Fig. 38, while the donor concentration near the surface will also be decreased. Although faster decay can occur, the principal decay effect observed has a time constant of the order of 10^{-3} sec at $1000°$ K.

These effects lead to considerable doubt as to the significance of d.c. measurement of work function. At higher temperatures the 'saturated' current density is higher, so that all three of the above types of poisoning are more severe; on the other hand recovery by reduction and electrolytic processes is also more rapid, and the 'saturated' emission depends on the balance between the two. The pulsed emission is of much greater physical significance, and the work function of about 1·5 eV is consistent with an electron affinity near 1 eV and a donor activation energy of a few tenths of an eV.

It is known from optical investigations[3] that the forbidden energy gap Q in BaO crystals is near 5 eV, that the electron affinity is near 1 eV and that donor levels are present 0·6 eV below the conduction band. Studies of single crystals have been made, but have not given results on conductivity consistent with the above, and have not therefore assisted in establishing the nature of the donor centres.

Thoria-coated Cathodes

These cathodes consist of a thin layer of thorium oxide powder applied to a refractory base metal such as tungsten or tantalum. The operating temperature is about 1600° C, but preliminary outgassing in high vacuum is necessary at about 1800° C. This also activates the emission, presumably by introducing donor centres and by tending to produce a surface layer with an excess of positive thorium ions. Heating to 1200–1400° C produces a much lower state of activation, while a brief heating at 2500° C produces a temporary state with higher emission. The stable state after activation at 1700–1800° C is represented by a Richardson equation with $A = 2·6$, $\phi = 2·5(4)$, while the temporary enhanced state has the same work function but a value of A about three times as large.

As with barium/strontium oxide cathodes, decay effects occur, though with a longer time constant ($\sim 0·1$ sec), and the coating is gradually lost during operation. There is considerable evidence that this is electrolytic in character, i.e. it depends on current density and may be much more rapid than the volatility would predict. The life of the coating is therefore adequate for many applications under pulsed conditions, but is too short for most purposes with direct current. At 1 amp/cm^2 the life may be only a few hundred hours, though there is a great deal of variation in this figure.

It appears that χ is of the order of 1 eV as for Ba/SrO, but that the donor activation energy is larger. The conductivity increases with the current drawn through the coating, and can lie between 0·03 and 1 ohm^{-1} cm^{-1} at 1627° C. The slope of $\log \sigma$ against $1/T$ is nearly 1 eV for the lower values, falling as σ rises. This type of variation does not occur in simple semi-conductors, germanium or silicon or III–V compounds, but is present in other oxide semi-conductors.

The life under d.c. conditions is improved by using a sintered mixture of thoria with tungsten or molybdenum powder. This is prepared as a ceramic and needs no base metal support. With an appropriate proportion of metal, the resistivity can be made suitable for direct heating by passing current through the ceramic. The work function is rather higher than the pure coating (2·8–2·9 eV), but this type of cathode is rugged and suitable for a variety of applications where the conditions are difficult, i.e. current density near 1 A/cm^2 d.c., high voltages, or imperfect vacuum.

REFERENCES

General References

BECK, A. H. W., *Thermionic Valves*. Cambridge, 1953.

DANFORTH, W. E., *Advances in Electronics V*. Academic Press, 1953, p. 170.

HERRMANN, G., & WAGENER, S., *The Oxide Coated Cathode*. Chapman and Hall, 1951.

WRIGHT, D. A., *Proc. I.E.E.* **100**, 111, 125, 1953.

(1) BECK, A. H. W., *Proc. I.E.E.* **106B**, 1959.

(2) LOOSJES, R., & VINK, H. J., *Philips Research Report:*, **4**, 449, 1949.

(3) APKER, L., TAFT, E. A., & DICKEY, J. E., *Phys. Rev.* **84**, 508, 1951.

TYLER, W. W., & SPROULL, R. L., *Phys. Rev.* **83**, 548, 1951.

TAFT, E., PHILLIP, H., & APKER, L., *Bull. Am. Phys. Soc.* II **3**, 46, 1958.

CHAPTER 10

Photo-electric Cathodes

One common photo-electric emitter is made by evaporating a layer of antimony on to a metal or insulating base and then allowing the antimony to react with caesium vapour at 100–150° C, until maximum sensitivity is reached, at which stage the layer has a 'deep ruby red' colour by transmitted light. The spectral sensitivity curve (a), (Fig. 39) shows a threshold near 6800 Å (1·8 eV) and a maximum at 4000 Å,

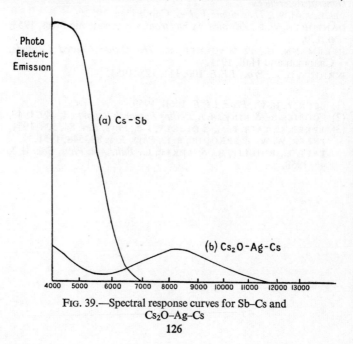

Fig. 39.—Spectral response curves for Sb–Cs and Cs₂O–Ag–Cs

although the yield remains high at least to 2000 Å. The sensitivity to 'white light'† is of the order 50 μA/lumen, and the quantum efficiency at 4500 Å may be from 20 to 30 per cent. The final layer has been shown to consist of very nearly one atom of Sb to three of Cs, although a slight Cs excess if common. At room temperature, the conductivity of the thin antimony layer first formed is about $3 \cdot 10^3$ ohm^{-1} cm^{-1} and falls on exposure to Cs at 120°C, reaching a minimum after a few minutes, at a value near $5 \cdot 10^{-4}$. The photo-electric sensitivity at this stage is about $0 \cdot 1$ μA/lumen, and the optical transparency is greatest at the minimum conductivity. On continuing the exposure to Cs, σ rises until when maximum sensitivity is reached, it is about $0 \cdot 1$. The time for full activations is five or six times that to give minimum conductivity. The layer at its maximum transparency is amorphous, and during the continued treatment, crystal growth occurs and considerable orientation develops. The crystals then consist of the compound Cs_3Sb, and the amorphous state must contain less Cs than this compound. The threshold of the photoeffect is established at 6800 Å as soon as any emission is measurable, thus the growth to maximum sensitivity is probably due to the increasing area of Cs_3Sb crystals.

In the final layer, the conductivity σ rises with temperature, with a slope of log σ against $1/T$ near 300° K of 0·35 eV, while σ at 290° K is about $0 \cdot 1$ ohm^{-1} cm^{-1}. The thermionic emission is given by $I = 0 \cdot 3T^2 e^{-1 \cdot 3/kT}$, and is 10^{-18} amp/cm^2 at 290° K. It appears that the layer of Cs_3Sb is a p-type semi-conductor, not n-type, in its final state of processing.[1] Sakata[1] measured the thermoelectric power and Hall effect, which indicate an acceptor concentration of 10^{20}/cm^3, and at room temperature a free hole concentration near 10^{16}/cm^2, and a mobility of 500 cm^2/volt-sec.

These results could be interpreted by a model (Fig. 40) in which R_1 is near $0 \cdot 6$ eV, Q is near $1 \cdot 7$ eV, and χ is small, at most a few tenths of an eV. This would explain the fact that the light-absorption, photo-conductivity, and photo-emission all have similar thresholds, near $1 \cdot 8$ eV, and it would also explain the high quantum efficiency, since this will be large when χ is small. The photo-electric behaviour is then attributable to the intrinsic properties of the Cs_3Sb crystals, only the

† This is defined for the purpose of specification as the light from a gas-filled tungsten lamp with its filament at a colour temperature of 2850° C.

conductivity being influenced by the presence of the acceptor centres. This is also in accordance with the high quantum efficiency. The situation here is similar to that described in Chapter 8 in connection with high secondary emission from insulators.

There are three general points to be noted in connection with attempts to develop models for photo-emitters. These make it difficult to be certain that a particular model is correct, so that although the

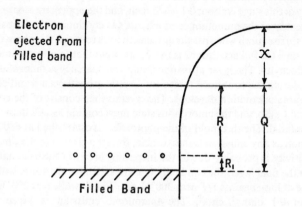

FIG. 40.—Energy levels in Cs–Sb photocell layer

above seems successful, it cannot be regarded as fully proven. The points are:

(i) In measuring photo-conductivity, it is difficult to avoid confusion with a current of photo-emitted electrons outside the material through the vacuum. If this confusion occurs, it is not surprising that the two thresholds are found to be identical.

(ii) There is an interaction possible between excitons and impurity centres, as found by Apker and Taft,[2] which can lead to ejection of electrons from the centres, and therefore to photo-conductivity, and perhaps to photo-emission. Thus excitons formed by incident energy P can move through the crystal and lose their energy by causing excitation of centres which they encounter. Photo-emission may therefore be observed with a threshold at energy P, which is not connected with the photo-electric work function. This has the value $\chi + Q$ for the main lattice effect, though a subsidiary effect may have a threshold at $\chi + R$, at temperatures such that the acceptor levels are occupied.

(iii) There is as with any semi-conductor the question whether the optical energy gap can be identified with the thermal energy deduced from conductivity measurements. There may be a difference due to the Frank–Condon effect, but the main problems are whether the conductivity is intrinsic or extrinsic, and whether the optical absorption corresponds with a direct or an indirect transition. This last possibility led Miyazawa[3] to suggest a model which differs from Fig. 40. However considerable further work is necessary on this type of semi-conductor to establish which model is correct. It may be noted that the absorption coefficient near the absorption edge follows the law $\alpha \propto (h\nu - Q)^{3/2}$, indicating a 'forbidden' direct transition which would support Fig. 40 as the correct model (Chapter 6, § 1).

Similar photocathodes are made using Na_3Sb or K_3Sb, or the three component compounds such as Na_2KSb. The threshold is near 4000 Å for Na_3Sb, 5500 for K_3Sb and 6000 for Na_2KSb. By adding a little caesium to the last of these, a still longer wavelength threshold and a larger quantum yield may be obtained.

Layers of Te may similarly be reacted with Cs or Rb producing compounds such as Cs_2Te with a threshold at 8200 Å (1·5 eV) and a quantum yield near 35 per cent.

A still more complicated behaviour is encountered in the cathode formed by oxidizing silver, allowing Cs to react with the Ag_2O, and then admitting further Ag to the surface. This process gives a cathode with spectral sensitivity as in Fig. 39, and with a sensitivity to white light of about 30 μA/lumen, and a quantum efficiency of 0·3 per cent at 8000 Å, The sensitivity is high in spite of low quantum efficiency because of the response to red light which is absent with caesium-antimony. The red response varies with the plane of polarization of the light, with the thickness of the layer, and with the Ag content of the layer. It is usually supposed that the red response arises from adsorbed caesium, and the blue from the Cs_2O formed in the reaction. The activated layer consists of silver atoms or small (colloidal) aggregates of atoms dispersed in a medium of Cs_2O. Whether Cs is also present, and if so in what form, is not definitely established. The optical properties of a thin silver layer in an amorphous state have been investigated and appear to be related to the red peak in spectral sensitivity. The conductivity is rather high, of the order 10^3 at room temperature and decreases as temperature rises, i.e. the behaviour is 'metallic'. The thermionic emission follows the equation $I = 0.1 T^2 e^{-0.75/kT}$, and is of the order 10^{-9} amp/cm^2 at 290° K. This behaviour might be described by a semi-conductor model as shown in

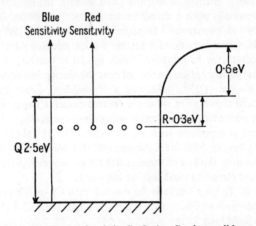

FIG. 41.—Energy levels in Cs$_2$O–Ag–Cs photocell layer.

Fig. 41, if we attribute the thermionic emission and the red response to impurity centres and the blue response to the Cs$_2$O lattice. The impurity centres may be formed by silver atoms dispersed in the caesium-oxide lattice, or the silver may form an amorphous colloidal structure, in which case the impurity centres are Cs atoms. Then the silver particles would form a structure in which a process which is really a surface effect can be produced throughout the thickness of a layer, converting it to a volume effect and ensuring useful energy conversion. The electron density in the Cs$_2$O due to the impurity centres is large, so that the quantum efficiency is not as high as in a poor conductor with a low value of χ.

REFERENCES

General References

SOMMER, A., *Photoelectric Cells*. Methuen, 1945.

GORLICH, P., *Advances in Electronics and Electron Physics XI*. Academic Press, 1959, p. 1.

(1) SAKATA, T., *Journal Phys. Soc. Japan*, **8**, 125, 272, 1953; **9**, 141, 1954.
   SOMMER, A., *Journal Appl. Phys.* **29**, 1568, 1958.
(2) APKER, L. & TAFT, E., *Phys. Rev.* **79**, 964, 1950; **81**, 698, 1951.
   APKER, L., & TAFT, E., *J. Opt. Soc. Am.* **43**, 81, 1953.
(3) MIYAZAWA, H., *Journal Phys. Soc. Japan*, **8**, 169, 1953.

Index